World Empires, World Missions, World Wars

Elementary Activity Book

NAPOLEON TO KOREA
by Diana Waring

1:1
answersingenesis®
Petersburg, Kentucky, USA

Special thanks to:

Len and Heather Armstrong, for their incredible help with the "biz";
Isaac's professors at Black Hills State University—thanks for understanding;
Kathy Follette, for her invaluable assistance in the library;
Melody Waring for her wonderful vocabulary games;
Michael Waring for his smashing food prep;
Bill Waring for editing, encouraging, and everything else that had to be done.

To our valued readers:

We care about the health and well-being of your students. Due to the physical nature of some of the games and activities, we would strongly encourage parents and teachers to exercise caution and diligence in oversight of the activities.

World Empires, World Missions, World Wars: Elementary Activity Book

Copyright ©2012 Diana Waring. No part of this book may be reproduced, stored in a retrieval system, or transmitted in any form or by any means—electronic, mechanical, photocopying, recording, or otherwise—without written permission from the publisher.

First printing: June 2012

For more information, contact
Answers in Genesis
2800 Bullittsburg Church Rd.
Petersburg, KY, 41080

All Scripture quotations are taken from the New King James Version, © 1979, 1980, 1982 by Thomas Nelson, Inc., Publishers. Used by permission.

Illustrations © 2012 Answers in Genesis unless otherwise indicated
P. 12 illustrations and ship map key icon © VectorStock.com
Map key icons © Jupiter Images Corporation

Cover Design: Brandie Lucas
Text Design: Diane King
Editors: Gary Vaterlaus, Anneliese Rumminger

ISBN: 978-1-60092-649-5

Printed in China

www.answersingenesis.org

Table of Contents

Note to the Teacher

Finally, a biblically-centered world history course for young children! And along with that, **it's fun**. This light-hearted approach to history makes a wonderful first impression on young children, allowing them to discover that learning is enjoyable: talking about people, solving word puzzles, making crafts, singing songs . . . all with the purpose of learning what God has done in history.

Our curriculum utilizes the latest information on how people learn best. Woven into its presentational fabric are the visual, auditory, and kinesthetic learning modalities and the four learning styles of Feeler, Thinker, Sensor, Intuitor (Meyers-Briggs system). You don't have to hold a PhD in educational psychology (or know anything about these various learning grids) to be able to use our curriculum— whether you do or not, you can rest assured that there will be a connection that appeals to each of your unique learners.

Feeler: A "People" Person

- wants to know the subjective, people perspective

Thinker: A "Facts" Person

- wants to know the objective, factual perspective

Sensor: A "Hands-On" Person

- wants to learn through hands-on, sensory experiences

Intuitor: An "Idea" Person
- wants to be involved in creative expressions

This *Elementary Activity Book* uses four phases per chapter, which correspond to the four learning styles mentioned above. Do not be concerned if you are unable to recognize the particular learning style of your student—this four-phase approach gives a wide variety of experiences, greatly enhancing each student's grasp of history in every time period. If you are simultaneously teaching older students using the *World Empires, World Missions, World Wars* curriculum, you will be able to easily and simply coordinate activities your younger students are doing with those of older students in each of the four phases.

Phase One is the **Introduction Time**, corresponding to the **Feeler** Learning Style. In this phase you will:

- read Bible stories and articles about important people
- share discussion questions
- discover "Fascinating Folks" & "Exciting Events"
- find suggestions for other books to read

Note: In the reading and discussion, create a comfortable atmosphere where your students can ask questions and explore ideas with freedom. Spread out the stories, one or two per day, unless your children are clamoring for more.

Phase Two is the **Exploration & Discovery Time**, corresponding to the **Thinker** Learning Style. In this phase, you will be playing with vocabulary words in:

- Scrambles
- Word searches
- Crossword puzzles

Note: Sit side by side with your students to do the vocabulary puzzles. Even if they don't know how to read, if they recognize some letters, you can solve the various puzzles. Chat together about the meanings of the vocabulary words until your children are comfortable with them.

Phase Three is the **Hands-On Time**, corresponding to the **Sensor** Learning Style. In this phase, you will:

- experiment with simple science projects
- create child-friendly crafts
- fix (and eat!) "Fun Food"
- color the maps or find your way through the mazes

Note: Take your time with these hands-on projects. We suggest that you only do one per day so your students have plenty of opportunity to enjoy the experience.

Phase Four is the **Expression Time**, corresponding to the **Intuitor** Learning Style. In this phase you may:

- create your own masterpiece
- perform in an "Acting-Up History" skit
- sing a "Somewhat Silly Song"
- rollick in "Rhyme Time"
- move in an "Action Activity"
- play a "Goofy Game"

Note: If you're doing "Acting-Up History," it could take an entire week to learn lines, make costumes, find props, and collect an audience. Some of the other expression activities could be accomplished in one session. The main point is to let the learning experience be enjoyable.

FAQs

Q. How long should we spend on each phase?

A. If you spend one week per phase, you would then complete each unit in one month, and the entire book would be finished in nine months. However, please feel free to take a longer or a shorter amount of time if that works better for your students.

Q. How long should we spend each day?

A. Young children should not spend hours per day on academic work, as they are not yet physically, mentally, or emotionally ready! Instead of coercing your impressionable learners into a formalized, regimented approach to education, our curriculum easily accommodates their own natural way of receiving information: we will be reading out loud, talking together, coloring pictures, making crafts, doing science experiments, playing games, singing songs, reading, and coloring maps. You could realistically spend thirty minutes, two or three times a week, and complete all the projects. However, if students are enjoying what they are doing and would like to continue "playing" with history, feel free to follow their personal timetable. They will learn and retain far more, and with more enthusiasm, than can be expected from the rigidity of a traditional curriculum.

Q. How do I test my children to see if they have learned enough?

A. Test them by listening to them: listen to their answers, listen to their conversations with others, listen to their questions. The discussion questions listed are to give you a start at dialoguing with your children. As both of you learn to share the wonder, it will be a growing experience!

Q. How will I know if they miss anything?

A. History is everything that has happened since the moment of creation until the present. It is simply too large a subject to expect that children (or adults) will know everything about it. However, I guarantee that few elementary age children will know as much about the Modern Age and missions as your children, once they complete this course!

AUDIO RECORDINGS!

Much of the foundational teaching for this book, as well as for the *World Empires, World Missions, World Wars* curriculum, is found in the four-disc audio series *What in the World? Volume Three.* We suggest that you use this audio presentation to gain an overview in your study of the Modern Age and missions. The recordings are interesting, exciting, and fun to listen to—even for students in the early elementary grades!

Napoleon & Early Missions

Napoleon Bonaparte

Bible Verses to Read & Talk About

The Reason for the Modern Missions Movement: Matthew 28:18–20

In 1792, William Carey (considered the Father of Modern Missions) wrote a short book about the obligation Christians have to go into all the world and preach the gospel. It electrified Christians throughout Europe/ Read together this passage of Scripture and talk about what you learn.

- Look up the word "authority." What does it mean? Who has been given all authority in heaven and on earth? If Jesus tells us in Scripture to do something, by whose authority do we do it?

- What did Jesus tell his disciples to do? Do you think this message applies to us, too? Why or why not?

Wars and Rumors of Wars: Mark 13:7–8

In the early 1800s, Napoleon took over much of Europe through the Napoleonic Wars. Until his war in Russia in 1812, most people considered Napoleon unstoppable. Read this passage of Scripture together and talk about what you learn.

- Who was talking in this Scripture passage? To whom was He speaking? What did He say?

- Why do you think people need to know about this? What do you think happens to people when they hear of wars all around? Do you think this Scripture would have brought comfort to the people of Europe? Why or why not?

Suggested Books for Reading Together

Napoleon Bonaparte by Brian Williams

A very brief biography for children, this book is filled with color drawings of Napoleon and his times. A good "primer."

Napoleon and the Battle of Waterloo by Frances Winwar

Written for younger children, this World Landmark book is a sympathetic look at one of the greatest conquerors of all time. If read aloud, it can be enjoyed by even the non-reader.

The Emperor and the Drummer Boy by Ruth Robbins

A children's picture book, this is a fascinating anecdote from the life of Napoleon. It permits us an interesting look at one of Napoleon's foibles—his lack of understanding of the sea.

New Orleans: Battlefields Across America by David C. King

This fascinating little book shows us the connection between Andrew Jackson, President of the USA, and the British soldiers who were veterans of the Napoleonic Wars. Remember, it's all connected!

Hero of Trafalgar: The Story of Lord Nelson by A. C. Whipple

As is true of all of the World Landmark Books, this is an excellent biography for children. Lord Nelson was England's hero and Napoleon's nemesis. Read more about him in this wonderful book! Again, if it is read aloud, the non-readers will be able to enjoy it.

Tecumseh: Shawnee Warrior Statesman by James McCague

Written for young children, this is an excellent introduction to one of the key players of the War of 1812.

Ludwig van Beethoven by Noemi Vicini Marri, translated by Stephen Thorne

Isn't it amazing to learn that Beethoven composed a symphony (Eroica) in Napoleon's honor? And that, when he learned of Napoleon's intention to crown himself as Emperor,

Beethoven furiously scratched out his name from the music! Learn more about this epoch-shaping composer in this excellent biography from the Why They Became Famous Series series. A great read-aloud!

Imprisoned in the Golden City by Dave & Neta Jackson

This Trailblazer Book presents historical fiction for children—the story of Adoniram and Ann Judson, who went to Burma as missionaries in the early 1800s.

Fascinating Folks & Exciting Events

William Carey (1761–1834)

Considered to be the "Father of Modern Missions," William Carey was a most amazing man. He was born in England to a poor family just as the Industrial Revolution was beginning. When William was fourteen, he was apprenticed for seven years to learn the shoemaker's trade. That doesn't seem like a promising beginning for a world-changer, does it? But when William became a Christian at age eighteen, he began to use his workbench for more than just shoes! He studied the Bible, seeking to understand its meaning. He began studying different languages, propping up his study books on the workbench. Eventually, he mastered Latin, Greek, Hebrew, Italian, and Dutch. He walked many miles every week to preach at different churches. Finally, he was asked to become the full-time pastor at a small church, and the teacher at a small school. While teaching geography—some of it based on Captain Cook's findings—William kept imagining what it would be like to preach the gospel in places around the world where no one had ever heard of Jesus. A book he published in 1792 electrified Christians all over Europe by challenging them to go throughout the world spreading the good news. The following year, he and his family sailed

to India to do just that. For the next forty years, William Carey was a tireless Christian minister to the Hindu people of India.

Napoleon (1769–1821)

When the French Revolution began in 1789, the common citizens became a mob of angry people intent on righting centuries of wrong deeds by the kings and nobility. Unfortunately, the situation quickly deteriorated into what we call "The Terror." Many, many people were killed during this time, including the king, queen, nobles, military leaders, professionals of all kinds, and even leaders of the Revolution! All of Europe was alarmed at this. Many countries formed armies to take over Paris and stop the Revolution.

However, on the French side, one lone officer seemed unbeatable. This was Napoleon Bonaparte, who quickly rose to command the armies of Revolutionary France. Everywhere he went, he won battles and brought cities and countries under his power—until he went to Egypt. Napoleon had huge dreams of taking over all of Asia and the Orient, beginning with the mysterious land of Egypt. Unfortunately for him, Lord Nelson of the British Navy burned all but two of the French transport ships, which caused terror among the French soldiers stuck in Egypt! Napoleon was able to find a boat back home but left his army behind.

When he got back to France, he decided to take over all of Europe, including England, as well. He was such an incredible military genius that he was actually able to conquer all of Europe and declare himself Emperor. However, since Napoleon was so bad at knowing how to fight on the sea, and the British Navy was so good, the French army was stuck on the European continent. Napoleon's military genius never had a chance to cross the English Channel for a battle. Napoleon was so angry with the British and with their boats that he decided to make a fortress out of all of Europe, not allowing the British to bring goods for trade anywhere in Europe. This blockade made the British so angry that they landed some soldiers in Portugal to attack France from that side. The Duke of Wellington, one of the generals in charge, was very good at military tactics and was able to "nip at Napoleon's heels." He caused Napoleon to make mistakes. Napoleon's biggest mistake was taking an army of 500,000 soldiers into Russia. The Russians had a plan— let the Russian winter kill the enemy! And it

worked. Napoleon escaped the cold with only 20,000 of his original army.

By this time, many people were tired of Napoleon. Lots of armies marched against him, his trusted advisors turned against him, and he was forced to "abdicate" which means, "quit being Emperor." The Europeans gave him his own little island to govern, complete with a tiny army and navy. After several months, though, he hungered for bigger things. While the countries of Europe argued over a peace settlement, Napoleon escaped from the island with 1,000 soldiers. When he arrived in France, many of his former soldiers joined him. He took over Paris without a fight and began to prepare for the battle he knew would come. Meanwhile, the Duke of Wellington gathered up a small army of inexperienced soldiers, many of them borrowed from other countries. The Prussian army marched with him, knowing they had to beat Napoleon quickly before he could gather up more soldiers. They faced him at Waterloo in a huge battle in 1815. We say Napoleon "met his Waterloo" because he was beaten there and sentenced to exile on the tiny island of St. Helena. He died six years later, but his legend carried on.

Cypher Wheel

Photocopy this page, and then cut out the two circles. Punch a hole through the center of each circle, then insert a brad to hold the two together, the smaller one in front. If *A=D*, then place the smaller circle so that the *D* lines up under the bigger circle's *A*, then decode the letters one by one!

- If you set your Cypher Wheel so that *A=L*, then "abolition" would look like this: lmzwtetzy

- If you set your Cypher Wheel so that *A=R*, then "artillery" would look like this: rikzccvip

- How would "missions" look if you set your Cypher Wheel so that *A=T*?

- Or if *A=B*?

- If *E=R*, then which vocabulary word would look like this: rkvyr?

Try writing some more vocabulary words in your own Cypher Wheel Code! See if your parents or brothers and sisters can decode them.

abolition	artillery blockade	Nelson	treaty
Carey	campaign (military use)	outlaw	victory
missions	constitutional exile	Rosetta Stone	Waterloo
pioneer	India	scorched	
society	Napoleon	slavery	

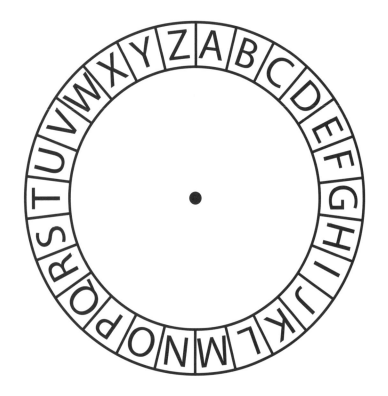

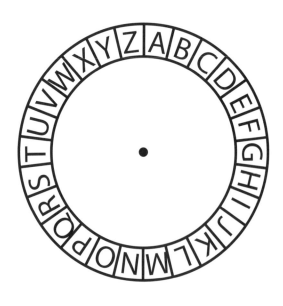

Hands-On History Fun

Create-A-Craft:

Printing with Potatoes

One of the most important tasks for William Carey in India was producing a Bible in the language of the Indian culture. He and two other missionaries worked hard to translate and print the Bengali Bible for the people. Try this "potato press" to see how it simplifies printing.

You will need:

- ½ potato per person
- Toothpicks
- Sharp knife
- Tempera paint, preferably a dark color
- Paper for printing

CAUTION: ADULT SUPERVISION REQUIRED. On one half of a freshly cut potato, use a toothpick to etch a block letter. Each person should choose a different letter, and at least two people should have vowels! An adult should very carefully use the sharp knife to cut away the rest of the top surface of the potato so the letter stands out. Dip the cut edge of the potato into the paint and press it onto the paper to print its letter. Working together, create "printed" words. You may enjoy making sentences with your potato presses!

Fun Food to Fix:

Curried Angel Eggs

When William Carey went to India, he experienced many different flavors. One of the most popular flavors in India is called "curry," which is a combination of several spices. Try this simple dish to see if you enjoy the taste of curry. We love it!

You will need:

- 1 egg for each person
- 1 tablespoon mayonnaise per egg
- ⅛ teaspoon curry powder per egg
- Salt and pepper to taste

CAUTION: ADULT SUPERVISION REQUIRED. Cook the eggs in their shells until hard boiled. Remove the shells and cut the eggs in half lengthwise. Preserve the shape of the whites as you carefully remove the egg yolks and place them in a bowl. To the egg yolks add the mayonnaise, curry powder, salt, and pepper. Mix well. With a spoon, put a dollop of the egg yolk mixture on each egg white. Serve immediately or refrigerate until eating time. Yum!

Marvelous Mazes!

Weave your way through Egypt with Napoleon. You will encounter the Pyramids, the sinking of Napoleon's ships at the Battle of the Nile, a desert oasis, and the amazing Rosetta Stone. Make sure to start at 1, and work your way to 2, then 3, and end at 4—don't take them out of order!

Your Own Masterpiece

Draw Napoleon as emperor of his tiny island, Elba.

Creative Fun with History!

Singing Somewhat Silly Songs:

Pop! Goes the Cannon

(to the tune of "Pop! Goes the Weasel")

Horatio Nelson was the British admiral sent to hunt down Napoleon's fleet during the Napoleonic wars. It was a good thing for England that Lord Nelson was so good at what he did! He destroyed the French fleet at the Battle of the Nile in Egypt, prevented Napoleon from invading England by chasing his fleet all across the Atlantic, and finally won the decisive sea battle at Trafalgar, though it cost Nelson his life.

First, Napoleon gave them the slip.
To Egypt he did wander.
But Nelson found them "sitting ducks."
Pop! Goes the cannon.

Next, around the ocean blue
Lord Nelson chased the French ships.
He didn't know just where they had gone.
Pop! Goes the cannon.

Chorus:

A plan to beat Napoleon's fleet;
A chance to win against them.
All depends on sighting ships.
Pop! Goes the cannon.

Chorus

Over to Caribbean Isles,
Lord Nelson tried to catch them.
But they were playing hide & go seek.
Pop! Goes the cannon.

Chorus

Back to Europe, floating their boats
As fast as they could sail them
To keep Napoleon out of England!
Pop! Goes the cannon.

Chorus

Finally, Lord Nelson did find
Napoleon's fleet a-sailing.
Trafalgar stopped the French on the seas.
Pop! Goes the cannon.

Industrialization & the Church's Response

Florence Nightingale

Bible Verses to Read & Talk About

God's Instruction for Us Concerning the Poor: Proverbs 14:21, 22:22; Isaiah 58:6–11; Luke 6:38; Galatians 2:10

During the Industrial Revolution in England, many people left their farms and villages to find factory work in the cities. Though they had been poor on their farms, in the cities they became destitute. Working long hours for very little pay and living in slums with almost no food, they were much poorer than before. See what these Scriptures have to say about helping the poor.

When you read these Scriptures, what do you learn about God's thoughts concerning the poor? What responsibility do we have? Does your church have a program for helping poor people? Is there something you can do?

What do you think God's attitude is toward people who consider themselves too important to care for the poor?

Suggested Books for Reading Together

***Watt Got You Started, Mr. Fulton? A story of James Watt & Robert Fulton* by Robert Quackenbush**

This interesting little book contains lots of information about these two pioneers of the Industrial Revolution. Did you know that Robert Fulton tried to interest Napoleon in his submarine, the Nautilus? Highly recommended!

***Boat Builder* by Clara Ingram Judson**

This is a younger children's biography of Robert Fulton. I found it especially captivating in the description of Fulton's submarine.

***The Thieves of Tyburn Square* by Dave & Neta Jackson**

Historical fiction for children, this Trailblazer Book describes the work of Elizabeth Fry to reform the prison system in England. Highly recommended!

***The Bandit of Ashley Downs* by Dave & Neta Jackson**

One of my heroes, George Müller, is the subject of this wonderful Trailblazer Book. George Müller was the man who set up orphan houses during the Industrial Revolution in England by praying in the finances to support them!

***Charles Dickens: The Man Who Had Great Expectations* by Diane Stanley & Peter Venema**

I love Diane Stanley's books! Her illustrations are wonderful, and the biography is well told. This is the story of Charles Dickens and his life. Highly recommended!

Fascinating Folks & Exciting Events

George Müller (1805–1898)

During the time of the Industrial Revolution, there were many orphans who lived on the streets of the big cities. They had no homes, no one to care for them, no love, and no opportunities. God used George Müller, a Prussian man in England, to care for thousands of these children. As you can imagine, feeding, housing, and clothing thousands of children took a lot of money! George was an unlikely candidate for handling large sums of God's money since, as a boy, he had been a thief. But when he was twenty years old, he became a Christian, and God turned his life around.

He had gone to England to study to become a missionary to the Jews and, though that original purpose had changed, he had remained in England to preach. George learned of a dentist, Dr. Groves, who had recently taken his family to Persia to do missions work. The unique part of Dr. Grove's story was that he was depending fully on God to support them—through prayer alone! That concept—trusting God alone to provide all that was needed—impacted George so greatly that, when he was asked to be the preacher of a small church, he agreed only on the condition he not be paid a salary. He and his wife wanted to experience the reality of seeing God meet their needs as they prayed and trusted Him.

From small beginnings come great things, and so it was with George Müller. After a few years of praying and seeing God's answers in practical matters, George felt a strong urging to open an orphanage in Bristol, England. The money to pay for the orphans' food, lodging, clothing, and schooling was all supplied by God as George prayed. After a little while, he opened another orphan house, and then another. Eventually, he had five huge orphan houses filled with 2,000 orphans who saw all their needs met as George and his staff prayed.

When George was seventy years old, he began to travel all around the world. He taught the body of Christ about the faithfulness of God by sharing how God had provided millions of dollars for the orphans in answer to prayer. And that is what we know about God working through a man who once had been a thief!

James Watt (1736–1819) & Robert Fulton (1765–1815)

These two men had a tremendous impact on transportation, manufacturing, safety, labor, war, and everyday life through their inventions! James Watt was a Scottish mathematical instrument maker at the University of Glasgow, which meant that he worked on mechanical "instruments" (not musical ones). One day, he was given a strange new contraption to repair, one using steam for energy to pump water out of coal mines. Though he was able to fix it, he was aware that the engine did not work as efficiently as it might. So, he pondered and thought, and thought and pondered, and considered what might be done to make it better. After years of working on the solution, James found a man who had the money to pay for the manufacture of a new engine—though they still weren't positive that it would work. However, it did work, and the Watt & Boulton steam engine, which was very powerful, very fast, and very efficient, changed the way people did their work.

Many new uses were found for these steam engines to power machines, and everything sped up! One of the most important uses of this new engine was invented by an American named Robert Fulton. He wanted to build a boat that was powered by steam. The first one he built didn't work—it broke in half and sank because of the weight of the engine. After rescuing the sunken steam engine, Robert built another boat—and it did work! Soon, he went back to America and built the *Clermont*, which was the first commercial steamboat in the world. This amazing 1800s invention truly ushered in the "Age of Steam"—steamboats, steam locomotives, steam printing presses, and full steam ahead!

Crack the Code

Using the key provided below, decode your vocabulary list. For each letter given, find it in the crossbars and replace it with the letter opposite it, so *A* becomes *D*, *E* becomes *G*, *F* becomes *H*, and so on. The first one has been done for you.

lpawrqsldi   industrial

lpxgpq   invent

msnfdpr   orphans

Bmoomamsg Ngssz   Commodore Perry

Kdndp   Japan

Himsgpbg Plefqlpedig   Florence Nightingale

pwsrg   nurse

udqq   Watt

Bslogdp Uds   Crimean War

rqgdo   steam

gpelpg   engine

Omsrg bmag   Morse code

Hwiqmp   Fulton

rwcodslpg   submarine

rqggi   steel

odbflpg   machine

fmrnlqdi   hospital

bdpdir   canals

umsjrfmn   workshop

riwor   slum

canals	Fulton	machine	steam
Commodore Perry	hospital	Morse code	steel
Crimean War	industrial	nurse	submarine
engine	invent	orphans	Watt
Florence Nightingale	Japan	slum	workshop

Hands-On History Fun

Create-A-Craft:

Finger Paint a "Seascape"

During this time in England, there was a very famous painter, Joseph Turner, who was best known for his paintings of the sea. Try your hand at creating a masterpiece!

You will need:

- ½ cup clear liquid dish soap
- 1½ tablespoons cornstarch
- Blue food coloring
- Green food coloring
- Freezer paper or other paper used for finger painting

Mix the dish soap and cornstarch together until well blended. Divide into two small bowls, then add the blue food coloring to one bowl and the green food coloring to the other. Mix with a spoon until the "paint" is smooth. On the paper (shiny side up), finger paint a picture of the sea using the blue and green paints.

Fun Food to Fix:

Nachos

Mexico had been a colony of Spain since the time of Cortes and the Aztecs. But when Napoleon placed his brother on the throne of Spain, the people in Mexico thought, "Enough is enough! Being ruled by Spain is bad, but this new king isn't even Spanish!" This began a series of struggles between Mexico and Spain that lasted for decades, even beyond Mexico's declaration of independence. One of Mexico's most important heroes in this struggle was a native Indian named Benito Juarez. He eventually re-established a republic. So, to remember Juarez, let's have Mexican food!

You will need:

- Tortilla chips (*several per person*)
- Grated cheese
- Sour cream
- Salsa
- Black olives, sliced (optional)
- Chopped fresh tomatoes (optional)
- Jalapeño peppers, sliced (optional—they're HOT!)

CAUTION: ADULT SUPERVISION REQUIRED. On a baking sheet, spread the tortilla chips in one layer. Sprinkle grated cheese over the tortilla chips (thick or thin according to your preference). Place in a preheated oven to 350°F, and bake for 10–12 minutes, or until cheese melts. Remove from oven and, using a spatula, carefully place a portion of chips on individual plates. Serve with salsa, sour cream, and the optional toppings.

Where in the World?

. . . is the Crimean Peninsula?

Color the areas around these:

 purple mountains   **green vegetation**   **yellow desert**   **blue water**

Clues for finding the Crimean Peninsula:

- I am EAST of Europe.
- I am SOUTH of Russia. I am NORTH of Turkey.
- I am SURROUNDED on three sides by the Black Sea.

Where am I?

During the Crimean War, Russia fought against Turkey, France, England, and Sardinia. France and England sent their ships through the Mediterranean to the Black Sea. Wasn't that a long way to go?

Your Own Masterpiece

Draw a picture of a yarn-spinning factory.

Creative Fun with History!
Acting-Up History:

Florence Nightingale & the Crimean War
Cast: Narrator, Florence Nightingale, Miss Social Opinion, Doctor Disapproval, Wounded Soldiers Chorus—each with appropriate bandages

Narrator:
In the year of our Lord 1853,
A war occurred right on the Black Sea.
It was Russia against Allies.
Now, to call them by name:
France, Turkey, England, Sardinia.
Yes, sir, they all came.

Florence:
In this horrible war,
Soldiers sickened and died—
Not only from battle
But from staying inside.
The hospitals—eeww!

They were rotten and rank
And filthy and nasty
And, frankly, they stank!

Miss Social Opinion: (taking Florence by the arm and walking with her)
But Florence, my dear,
Just what would you do?
No "nice" ladies work there.
From them, take your cue!

Florence: (removing Miss Opinion's arm and walking back to center stage)
Hmmph!
Well, we'll just see about that!

Narrator:
Florence Nightingale traveled away on the sea
To go to Crimea, bringing help rapidly.
And with her she brought
Other ladies to nurse.
So the soldiers got better
Instead of much worse!

Soldiers Chorus: (All together, with enthusiasm and much waving of casts and bandages)
Yay, Yay, she's got the stuff!
Yay, Yay, Florence is tough!

Doctor Disapproval: (moving to Center Stage)
Ahem!
Wait! Stop! Don't! No!
You ladies must leave now!
You ladies must go! (pointing off stage)

Florence: (moving in front of the Doctor)
S'cuse me, sir, really!
We're here now to work
And help all these wounded
To health, make them perk!

Soldiers Chorus: (All together, with enthusiasm and much waving of casts and bandages)
Yay, Yay, she's got the stuff!
Yay, Yay, Florence is tough!

Doctor Disapproval: (stepping to the side of Florence, gesturing to her)

Well, who would have "thunk" it?
These ladies have made
Such radical changes—
Many lives have been saved!

Soldiers Chorus: (All together, with enthusiasm and much waving of casts and bandages)
Yay, Yay, she's got the stuff!
Yay, Yay, Florence is tough!

Narrator:
The "Lady with the Lamp,"
As she's known now by all,
Changed hospitals greatly,
A complete overhaul.

Now our story is told,
Of blood, guts, and gore,
Of dear Florence Nightingale,
And the Crimean War.

The British Empire & Awakenings

Dr. Livingstone, I presume?

Bible Verses to Read & Talk About

God's Promise: Psalm 3:3–6

In this chapter, we will learn about the Christian missionaries who went to Africa to share the gospel. Read these Scriptures together and talk about what you learn.

When Mary Slessor went to Calabar (Nigeria), she left the comfort of the other Europeans with their protection and provision to go into the wild jungle and live among the native people. How do you think this Scripture applied to Mary? What exciting adventure could you imagine that would make this Scripture very important to you?

Those Who Share the Gospel: Isaiah 52:7–10; Romans 10:14–17

Whose feet are beautiful? What do these people bring? How does this apply to missionaries?

How many places in the world will see the Lord's salvation? How will the people hear the good news? What does that mean for us today?

Suggested Books for Reading Together

Queen Victoria by Dorothy Turner

From the Great Lives Series, this is a wonderful introduction for children to the longest-reigning monarch in English history.

Shaka: King of the Zulus by Diane Stanley and Peter Venema

A children's biography of a military genius, this is the story of the Zulu who united his people and turned them into the finest warrior nation in Africa.

Escape from the Slave Traders by Dave & Neta Jackson

Historical fiction for children, this Trailblazer Books title describes the work of David Livingstone to eradicate the slave trade in Africa. Highly recommended!

Trial by Poison by Dave & Neta Jackson

Another Trailblazer Books title, this is the story of Mary Slessor and her ministry in West Africa. She was an amazing missionary who lived among the tribal people of Calabar (Nigeria). Highly recommended!

Once Upon A Time! A Story of the Brothers Grimm by Robert Quackenbush

This is an absolutely delightful book about the two brothers who, through their thoroughgoing research, brought back many of the world's best fairy tales from their almost forgotten past. The Brothers Grimm lived in a German kingdom that was conquered by Napoleon, eventually ending up in Berlin at the invitation of the King of Prussia! Highly recommended! Great read-aloud.

Fascinating Folks & Exciting Events

Queen Victoria (1819–1901)

When Alexandrina Victoria was born, she was fifth in line behind her uncles and father to inherit the throne. It seemed that it would be a long time before she would ever be queen. However, her father and grandfather (King George III) both died when she was less than a year old, and the last of her uncles died by the time Victoria was eighteen. So she advanced to become Queen of England while still a mere slip of a girl! Now, Queen Victoria took her responsibilities quite seriously, working hard to learn all that was needed about politics and foreign affairs. When she was twenty, she married Albert, a German prince. Queen Victoria's favorite part of life was being a wife and mother. The people in England greatly appreciated having such a solid "homebody" on the throne; it was quite a refreshing change from many of the former monarchs! In 1851, Albert organized the Great Exhibition in London, which displayed the amazing inventions and discoveries of the Industrial Revolution. In six months, nearly six million visitors from all over the world saw the Great Exhibition, which was Albert's crowning achievement. When Albert died ten years later, Queen Victoria was so sad that she decided never to stop mourning. For the rest of her long life and reign she wore black dresses and lived her life as she thought Albert would have wanted. She also kept on working hard. During her sixty-four year reign (the longest in England's history), the British Empire grew to globe-size proportions. As they said, "The sun never sets on the British Empire," because England had colonies in islands and countries all around the world. Victoria was given the title "Empress of India," which pleased her a great deal. Her children and grandchildren became the reigning monarchs throughout most of Europe. In fact, Queen Victoria's reign was such a monumental, important time in England's history that the whole period took its name from her—The Victorian Age.

David Livingstone (1813–1873)

Can you imagine having to work fourteen hours a day as a ten year old? Or what about having your only chance for education by attending night school after your long hours at work? These were the experiences of a Scottish boy named David Livingstone. When he was twenty years old, David experienced a call of God to missions—to China, he thought. So he studied to become a medical missionary, but, because China was closed to missionaries in 1840, he was sent to South Africa instead. David Livingstone seems to never have missed going to China because he loved Africa and the Africans! He became one of the greatest explorers in the world as he hiked his way across much of the continent, keeping diaries of his experiences, writing scientific reports, and studying the various languages of the different tribal peoples. Even more important than his exploration, however, was his work to end the slave trade—the capturing and selling of African people. Though he is now remembered more as an explorer than as a missionary, he wrote in 1853, "I will place no value on anything I have . . . except in relation to the Kingdom of Christ." David Livingstone was so loved by his native friends that, when he died, they carried his body fifteen hundred miles to a ship on the coast of Africa so he could be buried in England— though his heart belonged to Africa.

Crossword Puzzle

Using the clues and the words from your vocabulary list below, fill in the crossword puzzle.

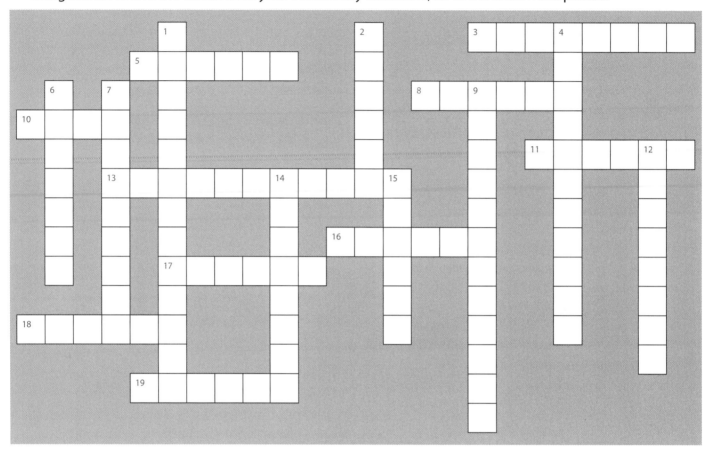

Across:

3. Buying and selling of goods between different places.

5. Wild land thickly overgrown with vines, bushes, and trees.

8. Wrote the book that popularized evolution.

10. The founder of communism.

11. The continent where Livingstone was a missionary.

13. Explored the African continent.

16. To bring in from a foreign country for sale or use.

17. Stanley tried to avoid _____ warfare in Africa.

18. The German king.

19. Of the indigenous people or customs.

Down:

1. Empress of India.

2. Group of people occupying the same region under the same government.

4. To make by machine (or hand).

6. A group travelling together for safety through dangerous country.

7. People who travel over little-known lands for the purpose of discovery.

9. In the natural state; not manufactured.

12. Territory distant from the country that governs it.

14. A race to possess land.

15. To send goods out of one country for sale and use in another.

Africa	Darwin	jungle	Marx	raw materials
caravan	explorers	Kaiser	nation	scramble
colonies	export	Livingstone	native	tribal
commerce	import	manufacture	Queen Victoria	

Hands-On History Fun

Science Stuff:

Just for fun, try this experiment with static electricity.

One of the most outstanding scientists of all time was also a devout Christian. His name was Michael Faraday (1791–1867), and his special area of interest, which changed the world, was electricity.

You will need:
- ½ teaspoon salt
- ½ teaspoon black pepper
- 1 plastic spoon
- Woolen cloth or yarn

Stir the salt and pepper together on a plate. Now, how on earth could you possibly separate them out again, back into their original state? Try this: Rub the spoon with wool. Then hold the spoon over the plate. What happens? Try holding the spoon closer to the mixture.

What happens now?

The explanation is that the plastic spoon becomes electrically charged when it is rubbed and attracts the pepper.

Fun Food to Fix:

Singapore Delight

The British Empire included many faraway, exotic places, which were very intriguing to the people of Europe. This pudding comes from an island known as Singapore, south of the Malay peninsula in Southeast Asia. It was once a part of the British colonies and continues to be a thriving center of commerce.

You will need:
- Instant coconut pudding
- 2 cups milk (or amount specified on box)
- 1 teaspoon vanilla
- ½ cup crushed pineapple (topping)
- 3 tablespoons shredded coconut (topping)

Make the coconut pudding according to the directions on the box, adding the vanilla to the mix. When it is set, divide the pudding into four bowls, then top with the crushed pineapple and shredded coconut. It's GOOD!

Marvelous Mazes!

Safari
with
Livingstone

YOU MADE IT!

Your Own Masterpiece

Draw a picture of the British Navy sailing the high seas.

Creative Fun with History!

Action Activity:

Globe-trotting Around the British Empire

"The sun never sets on the British Empire" was a phrase used to describe just how big the British Empire really was.

There were British colonies, protectorates, and other "empire" relationships in the Northern Hemisphere and Southern Hemisphere; in the islands of the Arctic Ocean, Atlantic Ocean, Pacific Ocean, and Indian Ocean; and on six of the seven continents—Asia, Australia, North America, South America, Europe, and Africa (Antarctica was not part of the Empire). This Action Activity, though it names only a few places in the Empire, will help illustrate how the British Empire covered one-fourth of the world, all around the globe!

You will need:

- A large playing area
- The map on the next page for locating the places
- A length of yarn or rope across your playing area to divide the Southern Hemisphere from the Northern Hemisphere
- Paper plate colored to look like the sun, with string attached like a necklace
- 10 paper plates, each labeled with a number and a country (see the chart below)
- 6 green pieces of construction paper and 4 blue pieces of construction paper labeled with a number and a continent/ocean and decorated as you please (see the chart below)

PAPER PLATE LABELS	«-»	CONSTRUCTION PAPER LABELS	
#1 – England	«-»	Green	#1 – Europe
#2 – Falkland Islands	«-»	Blue	#2 – Atlantic Ocean
#3 – British Guiana	«-»	Green	#3 – South America
#4 – Canada	«-»	Green	#4 – North America
#5 – Northwest Territories	«-»	Blue	#5 – Arctic Ocean
#6 – New Zealand	«-»	Blue	#6 – South Pacific Ocean
#7 – Australia	«-»	Green	#7 – Australia
#8 – Singapore	«-»	Blue	#8 – Indian Ocean
#9 – India	«-»	Green	#9 – Asia
#10 – South Africa	«-»	Green	#10 – Africa

Step 1: Label a plate and a green paper each with a big "#1," then label the plate "England" and the paper "Europe."

Step 2: Label a plate and a blue paper each with a big "#2," then label the plate "Falkland Islands" and the paper "Atlantic Ocean."

Step 3 through step 10: Continue down the chart, labeling plates and colored papers.

The green and blue papers will be arranged on the floor in this activity, and the matching plates will be set on them by each player in turn. The players will be globe-trotting west visiting each ocean and continent through ten locations that were part of the British Empire.

Have a leader, using the map below for direction, place each of the ten colored papers on the floor of the playing area. Use a large, spacious area, indoors or outside, so the players can move a lot. Be sure to place the continents and oceans in their respective hemispheres—on one side of the yarn or the other—arranged just as they are shown on the map.

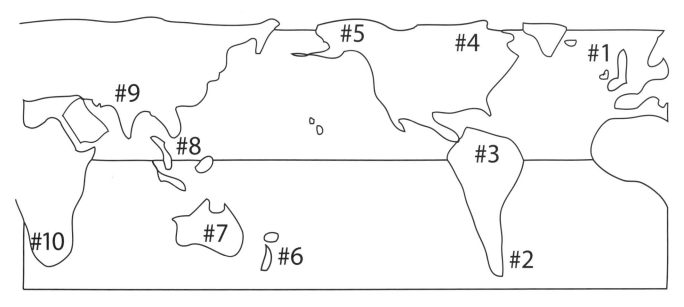

The play:

One player, holding the plates and wearing the "sun," begins on the side of the area and "globe-trots" over to "#1 – Europe." Setting the plate, "#1 – England" on it; the player then three times jumps in the air and shouts the name of the country. The other players then three times jump in the air and shout the continent or ocean. It sounds like: player—jump ENGLAND jump ENGLAND jump ENGLAND; others—jump EUROPE jump EUROPE jump EUROPE.

The same player continues to "Blue #2 – Atlantic Ocean," places "#2 – Falkland Islands" on it, and commences: jump FALKLAND ISLANDS jump FALKLAND ISLANDS jump FALKLAND ISLANDS; others—jump ATLANTIC OCEAN jump ATLANTIC OCEAN jump ATLANTIC OCEAN.

The first player continues through all ten locations in this manner. When the first player is finished and returns to the starting point, the second player takes the sun and the plates and goes globe-trotting. Repeat until all players have had a turn.

Variation: When the player lands at the location, he jumps up and down three times shouting the continent or ocean, while the others respond by jumping up and down three times shouting the country.

It would be an excellent addition to this exercise to have the students look at a large world map or globe and find the ten locations. How amazingly large the British Empire was! Just think, with all those countries, even if it were nighttime in England, someplace else the sun was shining on the Empire.

Napoleon III & Christian Outreach

Hudson Taylor

Bible Verses to Read & Talk About

Helping the Poor: Proverbs 14:31; Micah 6:8; Proverbs 22:22–23

Before the Salvation Army began, the poor and needy of England were without help. William and Catherine Booth, in founding the Salvation Army, focused on helping these people in their needs as well as sharing the gospel with them.

Read these Scripture passages together and talk about what you learn.

What does it mean to "oppress the poor"? What does Proverbs 14:31 tell us about those who honor God? How are these two attitudes and actions different from each other? What are some practical ways you can help the needy?

Suggested Books for Reading Together

Kidnapped by River Rats by Dave & Neta Jackson

Historical fiction for children, this Trailblazer Books title describes the ministry of William and Catherine Booth, the founders of the Salvation Army. Highly recommended!

Shanghaied to China by Dave & Neta Jackson

Hudson Taylor was an amazing missionary. You will enjoy reading about his life in this fabulous book in the Trailblazer Books series.

The Hidden Jewel by Dave & Neta Jackson

This Trailblazer Books title tells the story of Amy Carmichael and the work she did to care for the children of India. Wonderful!

Ahoy! Ahoy! Are You There? A Story of Alexander Graham Bell by Robert Quackenbush

I love this author! He includes fascinating little tidbits about the people in the time period, so that it truly comes alive.

Linnea in Monet's Garden by Christina Bjork, illustrated by Lena Anderson

This is a delightful book to use for introducing children to the paintings of Claude Monet. He was an impressionist painter who lived in France during this time period.

Fascinating Folks & Exciting Events

Napoleon III (1808–1873)

Louis Napoleon Bonaparte was the nephew of Emperor Napoleon I. After the downfall of Napoleon at Waterloo, France was again under the rule of a king. That meant they went from a monarchy (with a king) to a republic (because of the French Revolution) to an empire (with Napoleon I) and then back to a monarchy (with a king). However, after about thirty years, the people had had enough of the monarchy. They wanted a republic again and were willing to fight to get it. So the king fled, the republic was proclaimed, the assembly was elected, and Louis Napoleon Bonaparte was voted into the assembly on the basis of his famous name.

A few months later, he ran for president of the republic and won a smashing victory. But Louis Napoleon had more in common with his uncle than just the name. He saw visions of glory with himself as the emperor of a Second French Empire. So after four years of the presidency (where he had promised to uphold the republic!), he arrested everyone who would cause him trouble and had himself declared Emperor of the French. He took the new name Napoleon III (Napoleon II, son of Napoleon, had died years earlier). The interesting thing about Napoleon III was that, though he said when he became emperor, "The Empire means peace," he constantly plunged France into war! The French army was at war in the Crimea, in Mexico, and in Italy, and they finally went to war against the Prussians in the Franco-Prussian War of 1870.

That was an unfortunate mistake, because the Prussians vastly outnumbered the French and were also better trained and better equipped. Within three weeks, Emperor Napoleon III and 124,000 of his troops were defeated by the Prussians at a fortress called Sedan. They were forced to an unconditional surrender that ended the Second French Empire. The Prussians continued to wage war against other parts of France, laying siege to Paris, which is the very "heart" of the French. Paris finally surrendered to the Prussians, which ended the war. This very quick war had the astounding results of converting the French Empire back into a republic and converting the loosely knit German Confederation into the German Empire!

Remember: Monarchy - Republic - Empire - Monarchy - Republic - Empire - Republic

Hudson Taylor (1832–1905)

If you went as a missionary to a country where most people had never heard the gospel and considered you a "foreign devil," what would you do? In the mid-1800s, European missionaries in China dressed like Europeans, lived like Europeans, and acted like Europeans, all the while trying to teach Christianity to the Chinese. It didn't work very well! The Chinese thought that the Europeans looked incredibly strange in their weird clothes and ugly hairstyles. In fact, when the Europeans tried to talk to a group of Chinese people, their words were seldom heard because their appearance was so odd.

One man changed all of that. His name was Hudson Taylor. Hudson Taylor had been dedicated to the service of the Lord in China before he was even born! His parents had a heart for missions to China and passed that on to their son. Hudson had a strong conversion experience when he was seventeen and felt a call of God to China shortly after that. In order to prepare for service, he studied medicine in London. In order to train himself for hardship, he lived mainly on oatmeal and rice. In order to learn dependence on God, he gave away most of his money to needy people, then trusted God to supply his own needs. This rigid training was rewarded when he got to China. Hudson Taylor was able to live very simply and humbly while he got on with the business of learning the language and sharing the gospel.

One day he noticed that the people were staring at his clothing and not listening to his words. So, he decided to dress in Chinese clothing and to prepare his hair as the Chinese men did—with a long braid down his back! At first he had to use a fake braid, but eventually it was replaced with his own hair. The other European missionaries were horrified, but the Chinese were listening. They began receiving the wondrous message of Jesus that Hudson Taylor shared.

At this point, all the missionaries were living and working on the coastline of China because the interior of China was considered too dangerous and difficult. Hudson Taylor, however, saw that the gospel needed to go wherever the people were, so he prayed earnestly to see missionaries released into the interior. Eventually, he started the China Inland Mission, which was a non-denominational mission dependent upon God alone for financial provisions. That was very unusual in those days—to ask a missionary to leave home and family without offering them any salary! But God blessed the China Inland Mission tremendously, and people from many countries and many churches joined Hudson Taylor in the evangelization of the interior of China—all wearing Chinese clothes!

Word Search

Using the words from your vocabulary list at the bottom of the page, search for words in the puzzle. The words are diagonal, vertical, and horizontal. Have fun!

```
N C O N V E R T E D S V I U Y F V U R
A E L I Z O U S K Y A O T E J O O S W
T S V J H I L G D I U T Q U B A N D H
I P A A W G Y U A O V R Y I S N B M E
O O C I N T E R N A T I O N A L I F E
N K C W S G B D I T S K G L B Z S D O
A J I Z F Y E I E F E N L A K Y M Q I
T S N L V O N L W C I E M N C J A V O
E J E Q Z W R S I H V E R D H W R I T
L W G B M O O D Y Z I T M O I Z C R W
E Y L U V J O P K F E P A D N Y K E S
P K I D A I S R P A B A S R A B I E S
H P W A T O E U A U V S Z C I N E T M
O G Q U I T V S S E Q T E M P L E Y G
N S Y D M S E S T G L E K L W U D S O
E B M V O K L I J Y L U R B A N S Y B
H U D S O N T A Y L O R S W D E M F K
```

band	temple	urban	Prussia	Moody
evangelize	von Bismarck	vaccine	Hudson Taylor	rabies
opium	inland	China	volunteer	telephone
Roosevelt	Pasteur	international	converted	

Hands-On History Fun

Create-A-Craft:

Make a Musical Instrument and Join the Band!

William and Catherine Booth, the founders of the Salvation Army, realized that they would have to employ some unusual methods in order to attract the interest of the people who lived in the slums of England. So, they held open-air meetings using a band playing lively music to draw the crowds. It was a hit!

Make as many instruments as you have children (and willing adults!).

To Make a Kazoo:

Using an empty toilet paper roll or paper towel roll, wrap a piece of waxed paper around one end and attach it with a rubber band. Hum into the other end.

To Make a Guitar:

In the lid of a shoe box, cut a rectangular hole.

Wrap several different-size rubber bands around the box, making sure they go over the hole. Strum, strum, strum!

To Make a Musical Comb:

Cover a comb with tissue paper and blow through the paper. You may also try it with wax paper.

To Make a Finger Cymbal:

Ask at the hardware store in the nails and bolts display for some very large steel washers. Use string to hang them on your fingers.

To Make a Drum:

Bang a metal pan or a stout box with a wooden spoon.

Assemble your band together and play a cheering rendition of "When the Saints Go Marching In" around the house!

Fun Food to Fix:

Fruity Milkshake, á la Louis Pasteur

Louis Pasteur was the Frenchman who discovered how to "pasteurize" milk to destroy the bacteria that could be dangerous to people. He also discovered the rabies vaccine, disproved "spontaneous generation" through an experiment that has never been refuted, and avoided a national crisis—by saving the wine crop of France! To celebrate this amazing man's discoveries, let's make something wonderful from milk.

You will need for each serving:

- 1 cup milk
- ½ banana
- 3 ice cubes or 3 frozen strawberries (my preference!)
- 1 tablespoon sugar (optional)
- 1 teaspoon vanilla

In a blender, blend all of the ingredients until smooth. Drink immediately. Yum!

Where in the World?

. . . is China?

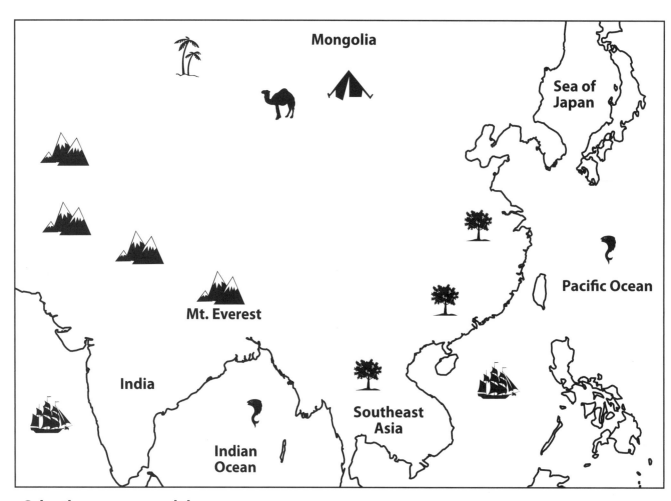

Color the areas around these:

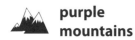 **purple mountains**

 **green vegetation**

 **yellow desert**

 blue water

Clues for finding China:

- I am WEST of the Pacific Ocean.
- I am NORTH of Southeast Asia.

Where am I?

- I am SOUTH of Mongolia.
- I am NORTH of Mt. Everest.

Your Own Masterpiece

Draw a picture depicting a Salvation Army band.

Creative Fun with History!

Rhyme Time:

Brrrrring - Bell
Or, Alexander Graham Bell and the Invention of the Telephone

One of the most amazing inventions of the 1800s was the telephone. Alexander Graham Bell, in his search for a means to aid the deaf, came upon various principles that made him think it would be possible for electricity to carry the sound of human voices. His experiments resulted in the invention of the telephone. Can you imagine what it would be like to not have telephones? It makes us thankful to think of the hard work done by Alexander Graham Bell!

Sitting in a circle, everyone claps slowly and rhythmically.
One - Two - Three - Four *(over and over, but don't count: only clap)*
The first player then says in rhythm with the clapping:
"Brrrrring - Bell."
Then the person to their right rhymes the last word (in rhythm with the clapping):

"Brrrrring - Yell." *(Any word may be used that rhymes with "bell.")*

Then, if successful in making the rhyme in time, the second person starts a new rhyme:
"Brrrrring - Phone." *(for instance)*
Then the person to their right rhymes the last word (in rhythm with the clapping):
"Brrrrring - Zone." *(Any word may be used that rhymes with "phone.")*

If the second player is not successful in making the rhyme in time, the first player says the rhyme again (in rhythm):
"Brrrrring - Bell."

Now, skipping over the person to the immediate right, play passes to the next person in line, who must respond with a rhyme.

Play continues around the circle until everyone has successfully rhymed some words.

A few telephone words to get you started rhyming:

bell	ring	friend	set	call	far	cord
phone	talk	sound	wire	dial	speak	tone

Alliances & Revivals

The Wright Brothers

Bible Verses to Read & Talk About

Who's in Charge Here? Daniel 2:20–21; Psalm 24:1–2; Romans 13:1–2

The early 1900s was a time of change. Read these Scriptures and talk together about what you learn.

What do these Scriptures indicate about who's in charge of the world?

When there are changes of kings and government, who is in control? What does that mean for us today?

Suggested Books for Reading Together

***The Wright Brothers* by Quentin Reynolds**

Well-written and interesting for children, this World Landmark Book is the story of the brothers who worked together to make a machine that could fly. If it is read aloud, even your non-readers will enjoy this story!

***Wings: The Early Years of Aviation* by Richard Rosenblum**

What a delightful book! Along with captivating illustrations, this book is filled with fascinating

bits and pieces of aviation history. Non-readers will enjoy seeing the pictures and learning more about airplanes. Highly recommended!

***Mask of the Wolf Boy* by Dave & Neta Jackson**

This Trailblazer Books title is a historical fiction account of Jonathan and Rosalind Goforth who lived through the Boxer Rebellion in China and went on to see a tremendous response to Jonathan's traveling evangelistic ministry. Excellent!

Fascinating Folks & Exciting Events

Balkan Wars (1912–1913)

These wars were little wars compared to most, but they ushered in one of the biggest wars ever—World War II. To understand them, you have to take a step backward in history, as well as a peek into geography. If you look at a map of Europe and the Middle East, you will see, at the southeastern end of Europe, an area known as the Balkans. It includes these places: Serbia, Bosnia and Herzegovina, Macedonia, Albania, Bulgaria, Romania, Montenegro, and Greece.

Way back in the 1300s, the Ottoman Empire, located in what is now called Turkey, conquered the Balkans and placed all the people under Muslim rule. After nearly 500 years of that, the people had had enough and began to desire independence. In 1829, Greece fought her

way to independence with the help of the British, French, and Russians. Serbia, Romania, and Montenegro were the next to gain independence in 1878. By 1908, Bulgaria had broken off from the Ottomans, while Bosnia and Herzegovina was "occupied" by Austria-Hungary. Are you confused yet? Just look at a map to see how close Austria-Hungary is to Bosnia and Herzegovina. Because many of the people in Bosnia and Herzegovina were of Serbian descent, Serbia did not like having the Austrians there at all. Serbia would have preferred to take care of Bosnia and Herzegovina herself, but the Austro-Hungarian Empire would not have liked that at all! Remember, Austria-Hungary was very big and powerful, and they were worried about the Serbians allowing their friends, the Russians, to gain more territory and power.

In those days, all the governments of Europe were concerned about something they called the "balance of power" (that means that no one had too much power, but that everyone had just enough—kind of like balancing on a seesaw). At this point, Albania and Macedonia were still under the control of the Ottomans. So Serbia and Bulgaria went together to attack Turkey and divide the rest of the Balkans between them. They went to war in 1912, which was the First Balkan War. The Ottomans were defeated. Now comes the crazy part: Serbia and Bulgaria could not agree on who got what part of the Balkan territory, so they decided to fight over it. That is how the Second Balkan War got started (in 1913). When it was over, Bulgaria had lost, which made Serbia very happy. All except for the issue of Bosnia and Herzegovina. But that is a story for another chapter!

Wright Brothers (Wilbur: 1867–1912; Orville: 1871–1948)

Birds make it look easy, but for humans flying was quite difficult to figure out.

The two men who first made it happen were Wilbur and Orville Wright from Dayton, Ohio. As boys, they were always investigating how mechanical things worked and trying their hand at designing their own machines (such as a machine that would fold newspapers!). They set up their own bicycle shop and made bicycles for sale, rather than purchasing them from a manufacturer. This "little hobby" soon took over all of their time and interest.

The Wright brothers, like many other inventors, wanted to figure out how to make an engine-powered flying machine. It was a race to see who could first discover how to fly a heavier-than-air contraption, and many people were hurt and killed in the process. Wilbur and Orville, in trying to invent a machine that could fly, relied on published information about different shapes and air pressure, until they realized that the published data were all wrong. Then, they built a "wind tunnel" in the bicycle shop to test different kinds of curved shapes. This allowed them to understand how to make the wings of the flying machine. Then they had to figure out how to deal with the extra weight of an engine, but this problem was also conquered. Finally, on December 17, 1903, at Kitty Hawk, North Carolina, Orville and Wilbur flew their flying machine. Free as a bird, at last!

Word Scrambles

Unscramble the words to spell out people, places, or things that have to do with your study of the turn of the century. Look at the vocabulary list at the bottom for possible answers, and don't get too mixed up!

sbaalkn _____

rusias _____

llaiance _____

dialcor _____

thiwrg borthres _____

neaplair _____

roxeb reilebnoi _____

miliathue _____

cupanotioc _____

biaser fromre _____

srefs _____

shopilyhop _____

icalrad _____

erndom _____

lanceab fo erpow _____

mottona _____

racz _____

trikes _____

iec-reef rotp _____

cordial	Serbia	Wright Brothers	**strike** (like a workers' strike)
Ottoman	ice-free port	Balkans	
Russia	radical	Boxer Rebellion	**occupation** (when one country "occupies" another)
humiliate	serfs	modern	
philosophy	czar	reform	

Hands-On History Fun

Create-A-Craft:

Make a Super-Duper Paper Airplane!

Orville and Wilbur Wright experimented with different shapes of wings to learn what would best support the weight of an engine and a man. Try your hand at making your own "unusual" airplane wings!

You will need for each participant:

- 8½" x 11" paper, cut in half to measure 4¼" x 11"
- Tape

Follow the drawings to make your airplane.

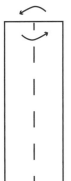

Fold along the dotted line, then unfold again

Fold along the dotted line to center

Fold along the dotted line to center

Fold along the original center fold

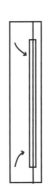

Fold the folded edge down

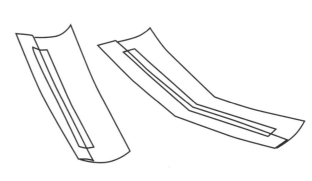

"Camber," or bend, the wing by pulling taped edge between thumb and fist

Crease slightly at center. Hold top and bottom with thumb and finger, and gently release.

Fun Food to Fix:

Linzertorte Look-Alike from Austria

Austria-Hungary was run by the longest-ruling monarch in European history—Emperor Franz Joseph. His reign lasted sixty-eight years—five years longer than Queen Victoria's! Linzertorte is one of the specialty desserts of Austria, fit for an emperor.

You will need for each person:

- 2 almond shortbread cookies
- 1 tablespoon raspberry jam
- Dusting of powdered sugar

For each serving, place the jam on top of one cookie. Dust with powdered sugar. Cover with the second cookie. Enjoy.

Where in the World?

...are the Balkans?

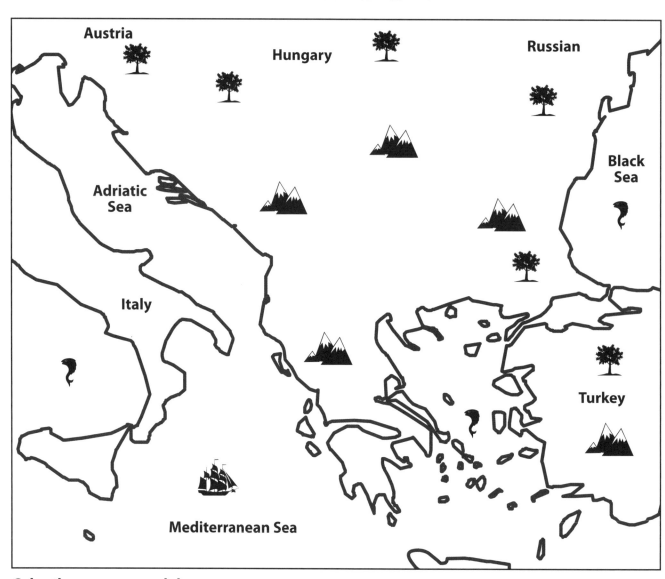

Color the areas around these:

 purple mountains   **green vegetation**    **blue water**

Clues for finding the Balkans:

- We are NORTH of the Mediterranean.
- We are EAST of the Adriatic Sea.

- We are WEST of Turkey.
- We are SOUTH of Austria, Hungary, and Russia.

Where are we?

Your Own Masterpiece

Draw your own flying machine.

Creative Fun with History!

Going Goofy Games:

The Triple Alliance & the Triple Entente Cordiale—Race to the Finish Line

To see which political relationship can really "go the distance," you need two teams to represent:

The Triple Alliance

- Germany
- Austria-Hungary
- Italy

The Triple Entente Cordiale

- France
- Russia
- Britain

If you only have two players, each will represent one team and hop alone—each player takes the name of one country.

If you have four players, two will hop together as one team—each player chooses a different country, representing four countries altogether.

If you have six players, three will hop together as one team—each player chooses a different country, representing six countries altogether.

For each participant, you will need three double sheets of newspaper, rolled up hard and firmly taped or tied with string.

Two lines are marked on the ground thirty feet apart and directly opposite each other. Have the two teams line up behind the first line. Each participant should place the newspaper "roll" between his ankles. No one should handle the newspaper once they begin hopping.

To begin the race, the first person of the team, naming his country and team, bends over and grabs his knees. The second person in the team, naming country and team, puts her hands on the first person's shoulders. The third person in the team, naming country and team, puts his hands on the second person's shoulders. Then, all together, the team should call out their name, either "Triple Alliance!" or "Triple Entente Cordiale!" An adult should signal the start of the race by shouting, "Go!" At this, both teams begin hopping to the other line. The first team to cross the line wins. If, during the race, anyone drops a newspaper, the team must stop, hop back two hops, replace the newspaper, and continue the race.

World War I & Russian Revolution

Lawrence of Arabia

Bible Verses to Read & Talk About

Our Deliverer in Time of War: Psalm 27:1–5, 140:1–2

World War I was an unbelievable time of upheaval and distress for much of the world. It was so horrible that many people who had previously believed that man was basically good changed their minds.

Read these Scriptures together and talk about what you learn.

What do these Scripture passages talk about? To whom is the Psalmist looking for deliverance? Was the Psalmist afraid? Why or why not? What can we learn from this attitude?

Suggested Books & Videos for the Whole Family

World War I by Ken Hills

This is an excellent "primer" of WWI for younger children. This Wars that Changed the World series volume is filled with illustrations.

The World War I by Martin Windrow

This is a very concise, simple look at the different parts of World War I, written and illustrated for children. It's another excellent primer of the war for elementary children in the Tommy the Soldier Through The Ages series.

Russia by Harlinah Whyte

This fun children's book is from the Festivals of the World series and includes a craft project of making "matryoshka" dolls—traditional Russian toys.

Sergeant York (video)

This video, telling the true story of Sergeant York, is amazing! As a Christian, he was not sure that it was right to go off to war. The movie shows how he resolved this issue, and what the incredible results were. Highly recommended for the whole family!

Fascinating Folks & Exciting Events

WWI (1914–1918)

Do you remember from the last chapter that Serbia was unhappy about Austria-Hungary occupying Bosnia and Herzegovina? Well, in June, 1918, Serbia's unhappiness spilled over into war! Archduke Francis Ferdinand, heir to the throne of Austria-Hungary, was assassinated during a parade in Bosnia and Herzegovina. The man who killed him was a Serbian nationalist who wanted Austria-Hungary out of the picture. This made Austria-Hungary really angry, and on July 28, 1918, they declared war on Serbia. Russia, good friend of Serbia, began mobilizing its troops to help little Serbia fight big Austria-Hungary. So Austria-Hungary's good friend Germany declared war on Russia! Now, this part is going to get a little crazy, so hold onto your hat. Because Russia was good friends with France, Germany decided to declare war on France, too. If you look at a map, you will see that Germany sits between France and Russia. So, Germany decided that it would be a good idea to quickly attack and defeat France before Russia was ready to attack Germany.

Unfortunately, in Germany's plan to attack France, it sent soldiers through Belgium, which was a "neutral" country (meaning a country not involved in a war). When Germany marched through Belgium on the way to France, Britain (the good friend of France) declared war on Germany! The friendly countries on one side were called the "Allies," and they included France, Britain, Russia, Serbia, Greece, and Italy. Other British Commonwealth countries, such as Canada, South Africa, Australia, and New Zealand, also entered the war on the side of the Allies. The countries on the other side of the war, who were friendly with each other, were called the "Central Powers," and included Germany, Austria-Hungary, Bulgaria, and the Ottoman Turks. At the beginning of the war, the United States did not have an official opinion about which side to support. After a while, though, German submarines began to sink American ships bringing supplies to the Allies. This made the U.S. angry, so the U.S. military entered the war on the side of the Allies in 1917.

World War I was a war of "firsts": the first time "underwater boats" (submarines) were used in a war; the first time airplanes were used in a war; the first time tanks were used in a war; and the first time a war was fought mainly from trenches—ditches dug in the ground where the soldiers stayed. Both sides had their own series of trenches, and the land in between was known as "no-man's-land." When the order came to attack, the soldiers on one side would come up out of their trenches and head across no-man's land to the trenches on the other side. Unfortunately, those soldiers would almost always be killed since the soldiers on the other side would simply point their guns over the top of their trenches and shoot. Both sides kept trying . . . and dying. More than ten million people died in the four years of WWI—called "the war to end all wars."

And just how did this war end? Russia experienced a revolution, so they quit fighting and left the Allies shorthanded. As Germany was mobilizing all of its soldiers to punch through the Allied lines and win the war, the U.S. joined the fray on the side of the Allies. The U.S. soldiers were fresh, not having experienced the death and destruction of the past three years, and with that "new blood," the Allies were finally able to beat the Germans in a few huge battles. The head of the German government, Kaiser Wilhelm II, decided it was over and fled to Holland. An "armistice" (agreement to end the war) was signed punishing Germany for its part in the war. We'll see what *that* led to!

Pigpen Puzzle

The key provided near the bottom shows the code—the alphabet placed within special shapes. Your vocabulary words are spelled out in the Pigpen Puzzle, but only the code shapes are given. You must decode each line by supplying the letter that belongs in each code shape. The symbols without dots represent the letters *A–M*; the symbols with dots represent the letters *N–Z*.

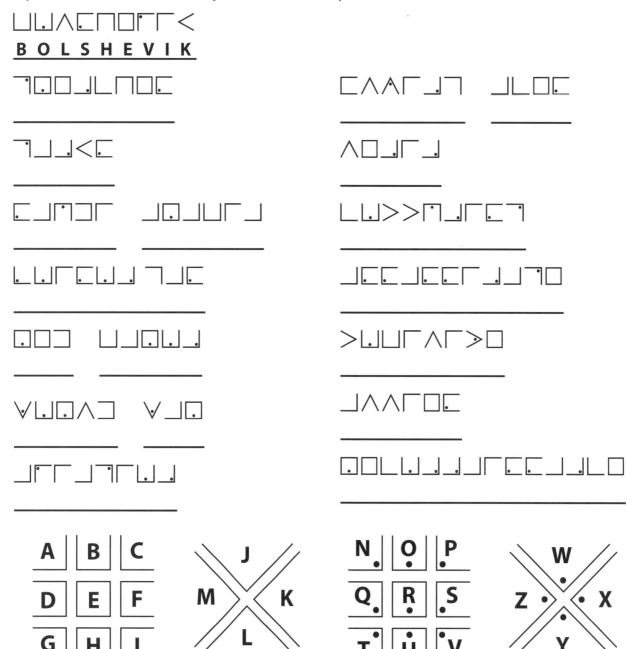

B O L S H E V I K

allies   Bolshevik   Lenin   reconnaissance   tanks

assassinate   communist   mobilize   Red Baron   trenches

aviation   flying aces   poison gas   Saudi Arabia   world war

Hands-On History Fun

Create-A-Craft:

Sand-tacular Greeting Cards!

During WWI, one of the most famous heroes was a British soldier named T. E. Lawrence. He helped the Arabs to fight the Turks and Germans in Mesopotamia, which really annoyed the Central Powers . . . and helped the Allies in Europe a great deal. Lawrence became known as "Lawrence of Arabia" because he lived and fought as the Arabs did. This included riding on camels through the deserts of sand, sand, and more sand! To remember his great exploits, let's do a sand craft.

You will need:

- ½ cup flour
- ½ cup salt
- 1 tablespoon sand
- ½ cup water
- ¼ cup tempera paint, whichever color you desire
- Zipper-type plastic bag
- Several sheets of white card stock, cut and folded to greeting card size

Place the dry ingredients in the plastic bag, then add water and paint. Seal the plastic bag carefully and gently knead the bag until the paint is smoothly mixed. With scissors, cut a small hole in one corner of the bag. This becomes your spout. Now, as if you were decorating a cake, decorate one side of each of the white cards. Let it dry 24 hours or until dry. Add your own personal greetings and send to a friend or family member!

Fun Food to Fix:

Russian Cucumber Salad

In 1917, the peasants in Russia, starving and upset at the enormous Russian losses in the war, revolted against the government of the czar, forcing him to give up his throne. In the chaos and confusion that followed, a revolutionary named Lenin schemed and plotted to overthrow the new democratic government. In an action known as the Bolshevik Revolution, Lenin and his communist government took over. The first thing they did was to end Russia's involvement in WWI. The second thing they did was to end all resistance to their rule. Russia remained under Communist control until the 1990s.

You will need:

- 1 cucumber, thinly sliced (peel if the skin is bitter)
- ½ teaspoon salt
- ¼ cup sour cream
- 1 teaspoon sugar
- ¼ teaspoon pepper
- 1 tablespoon apple cider vinegar (or other mild vinegar)

Place the cucumber in a shallow dish and sprinkle with the salt. Let it sit for one hour. Pour off the liquid, and pat the cucumber dry with a paper towel. Combine the other ingredients, mix well. Place the cucumbers in an attractive bowl and cover with the mixture. Make sure that all of the cucumber slices are enveloped in the dressing. Salt to taste. Chill for thirty minutes to one hour. Serve cold.

Where in the World?

. . . was World War I?

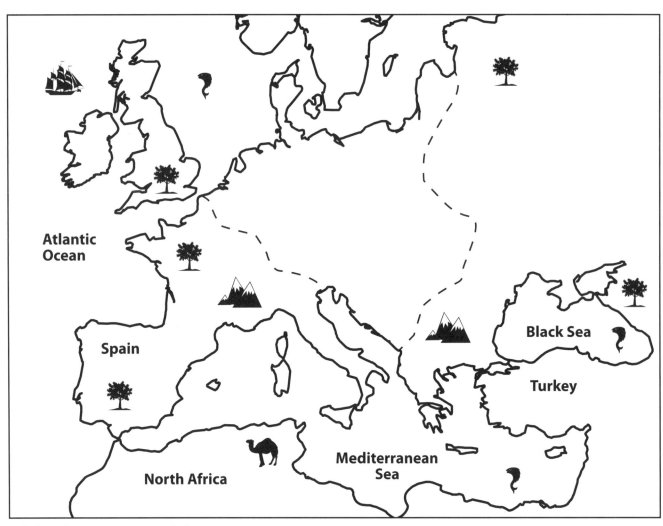

Atlantic
Ocean

Spain

Black Sea

Turkey

North Africa

Mediterranean
Sea

Color the areas around these:

 purple mountains   **green vegetation**   **yellow desert**   **blue water**

Clues for finding the Western Front and Eastern Front of World War I:

Western Front:

- My trenches are BETWEEN France and Germany.

- France is NORTH of Spain.

- France is EAST of the Atlantic Ocean

Where am I? Color me blue.

Eastern Front:

- My trenches are BETWEEN Germany and Russia.

- Russia is NORTH of the Black Sea.

- Germany lies BETWEEN France and Russia.

Where am I? Color me red.

Your Own Masterpiece

Draw a picture of a submarine under the water.

Creative Fun with History!

Singing Somewhat Silly Songs:

Lawrence of Arabia

(to the tune of "Oh, My Darling, Clementine")

Chorus:
Where is Lawrence,
Where is Lawrence,
Lawrence of Arabia?
Riding camels 'cross the desert.
Lawrence of Arabia!

He was British, helped the Arabs
With their fight against the Turks.
Blew the trains up, and the railroad,
And the bridges—the whole works.

Chorus

Then he whupped 'em at the Red Sea,
Took the Port of Akaba,
And the vict'ry was quite good for
Arabs and Arabia!

Chorus

Now, the Germans and the Turkish
Wanted Lawrence to be dead.
So they offered up a reward,
Placed a bounty on his head.

Chorus

To Damascus—throw the Turks out—
What a wondrous spectacle!
Freedom for the Arab people
Lawrence wanted most of all.

Chorus

At the finish of the World War,
Lawrence pleaded for his friends.
But the European countries
Took Arabia in the end.

Facism & Fundamentals

Eric Liddell

Bible Verses to Read & Talk About

The Downfall of Pride: Proverbs 8:13, 16:18

Between World War I and World War II, a new idea about how a nation should be governed came into being. This new idea, Nazism, was based on the concept that the German people were a "master race"—that they were much better in every way than other people. Read these Scripture passages together and talk about what you learn.

What do these Scriptures say about pride? What is God's attitude toward pride? What do you think the difference is between the pride of the Nazis and the pride in doing your chores excellently?

Suggested Books & Videos for the Whole Family

Hitler Youth by R. Conrad Stein

The youth of Germany were drawn into Nazism through the Hitler Youth Club. This World at War series book tells what happened to them.

Chariots of Fire (video)

This video tells the incredible story of Eric Liddell and his Christian witness at the 1924 Paris Olympics. For the whole family!

Fascinating Folks & Exciting Events

Eric Liddell (1902–1945)

Born in China to Scottish missionaries, Eric Liddell was a sickly child. It seemed that whatever illness came around, Eric caught it. One time he was so sick that a doctor told his mother, "Your son may not live through this, and if he does, he will never walk." The doctor was wrong—this young child went on to race in the Olympics, and win!

When Eric was five years old, the family traveled back to Scotland for a furlough. His parents returned to China without Eric and his brother because they remained in London for schooling. The headmaster of the Mission Society School believed that fresh air and sports were next to godliness! So he had Eric in outdoor sports several times a week. That was just the prescription for Eric Liddell. He thrived on running, his favorite sport, as well as playing rugby and cricket. When Eric went to university, though, he intended to pursue strictly academics since he would be returning to China as an instructor of science. A friend pointed out to him that he would study better if he took a break for sports, so he turned out for a race. The participants in the race included the Scottish Champion runner . . . and Eric beat him! He continued to race and play rugby for his university, and he continued to win.

Next, Eric was invited to be part of the British Olympic team for the 1924 Olympics in Paris. He was to run the 100-meter sprint—his best race. It was a near certainty that he would win the gold medal. When the race schedule was published, however, Eric saw that the 100-meter preliminary race would be run on a Sunday. God's command "Remember the Sabbath and keep it holy" was very important to Eric, and he felt it would be wrong to race on a Sunday. So he refused to run.

People were astonished, dismayed, upset, and angry at his refusal. The newspapers called him names. It was a very hard time, but Eric knew that God was first in his life, so he did not change his mind. The Olympic committee decided to give Eric the 400-meter run instead, though they knew that it was a completely different kind of race and that Eric had little hope of winning. Eric entrusted himself to God and prepared for the race. Just before the start, someone gave him a slip of paper with a very encouraging message. It said, "He that honors Me, I will honor." Well, against all odds, Eric won that race! Then he was considered a hero.

Soon, Eric returned to China and became a Christian teacher at a school for the children of Chinese diplomats, government workers, etc. During WWII, Eric remained in China, where he was eventually captured by the Japanese and was forced to stay in a prison camp. He continued to teach science to the children in the camp, though they had no microscopes or other scientific equipment. He also organized games, races, and as many fun times as possible for the people of the camp. Just prior to the end of WWII, Eric Liddell died of a brain tumor and finished his earthly race.

Cameron Townsend (1896–1982)

Along with William Carey and Hudson Taylor, Cameron Townsend was one of the most significant missionaries in the last two hundred years. The insight he brought to missions was pivotal for reaching the world with the gospel. What was this insight? Read on . . .

Born in the United States, Cameron Townsend went to Guatemala in 1917 as a missionary distributing Spanish Bibles. Soon after he began working with the indigenous people, he was stopped in his tracks by this simple question: "If your God is so smart, why can't He speak our language?" Though the mission had Spanish Bibles, they did not have Bibles translated into the language of these 200,000 tribal people. In response to this need, he translated the Bible for that tribe and also started a ministry focused on the needs of Bible translation throughout the world. This ministry is now known as Wycliffe Bible Translators. Cameron Townsend used to say, "The greatest missionary is the Bible in the mother tongue. It never needs a furlough and is never considered a foreigner." Now, Wycliffe Bible Translators, the largest independent Protestant mission organization in the world, has translators throughout the nations bringing the Word of God to people in their own languages. The ongoing task is to finish the work on the 3,000 languages remaining untranslated.

Cypher Wheel

Photocopy this page, and then cut out the two circles. Punch a hole through the center of each circle, then insert a brad to hold the two together, the smaller one in front. If A=D, then place the smaller circle so that the D lines up under the bigger circle's A, then decode the letters one by one!

- If you set your Cypher Wheel so that A=Q, then "Aryan" would look like this: **Qhoqd**

- If you set your Cypher Wheel so that A=J, then "anti-Semitism" would look like this: **jwcr-Bnvrcrbv**

- How would "dictator" look if you set your Cypher Wheel so that A=F?

- Or if A=X?

Try writing some more vocabulary words in your own Cypher Wheel code! See if your parents or brothers and sisters can decode them.

anti-Semitism	Hitler	pacifist	solution
Aryan	homeland	pact	Stock Market Crash
chancellor	immigrate	purge	superinflation
dictator	Nazism	racism	violation
fascism	nonaggression	Reich	Zionist

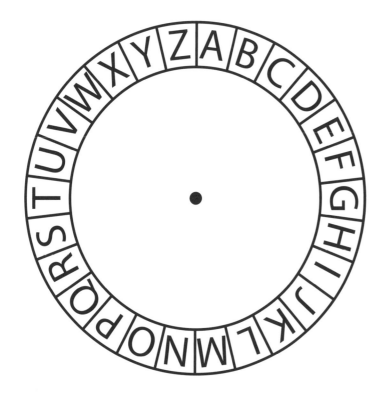

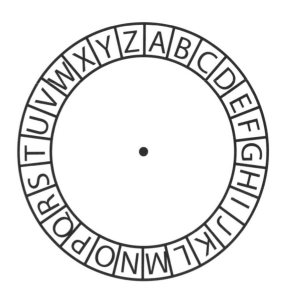

Hands-On History Fun

Create- A -Craft:

Making a "Ruby" Necklace

In this time period, many countries that had been under European colonization sought their freedom. One of the largest countries involved in this was India. India was considered the "jewel in the crown" of the British Empire, but the people in India were tired of being ruled by another country. So they did everything they knew to try to convince Great Britain to let go of this prized colony, and, eventually, it worked. It was the custom of the women of India to wear jewelry, which displayed their family's wealth. Let's try our hand at making a "jeweled" necklace.

You will need:

- 1 cup rock salt
- 4 drops red food coloring
- ¼ cup white glue
- Length of string for necklace—12" to 15"

Cover a cutting board with wax paper. On the wax paper, combine the rock salt and red food coloring. When it is well mixed, add the glue and continue squishing it with your fingers for two or three minutes. Next, lay the string out on the wax paper. Put ruby size bits of the mixture on two-inch portions of the string, with spaces before and after. Leave a short section on both ends so you can tie the necklace. Let the necklace dry. Tie the ends. Voila!

Fun Food to Fix:

Fresh Fruit Salad from Israel

During World War I, the British signed an agreement called the "Balfour Declaration of 1917," which was in favor of giving the Jewish people a national homeland in Palestine. This opened the door for many European Jews to begin moving to Palestine and setting up farms.

One of the most amazing results of this was that the desert began to "bloom"—fruits and vegetables grew and thrived under the careful tending of these Jewish farmers. Today, fresh fruits are a favorite in the nation of Israel with citrus fruit as a required ingredient in any fresh fruit salad.

You will need:

- ½ grapefruit
- 1 tart apple
- ½ cup raisins
- ½ tablespoon lemon juice
- 2 oranges
- 1 pear
- ½ cup orange juice
- 1 tablespoon sugar

Peel oranges and grapefruit. Wash and core apples and pears. Section the grapefruit, removing the white membranes. Put in a salad bowl, along with the orange, thinly sliced crosswise. Cut the apples and pears into small cubes and add to the bowl. Combine the remaining ingredients and pour over the salad. Mix lightly. Cover and refrigerate for at least an hour. Serve cold.

Marvelous Mazes!

Following the Balfour Declaration of 1917, Jewish families all over Europe began moving back to Israel, the Holy Land.

On the map below, there are three different Jewish families trying to get to Israel.

Use a different color of crayon to follow each family's route to Israel.

You know they have arrived safely when you reach the X.

Don't get too confused!

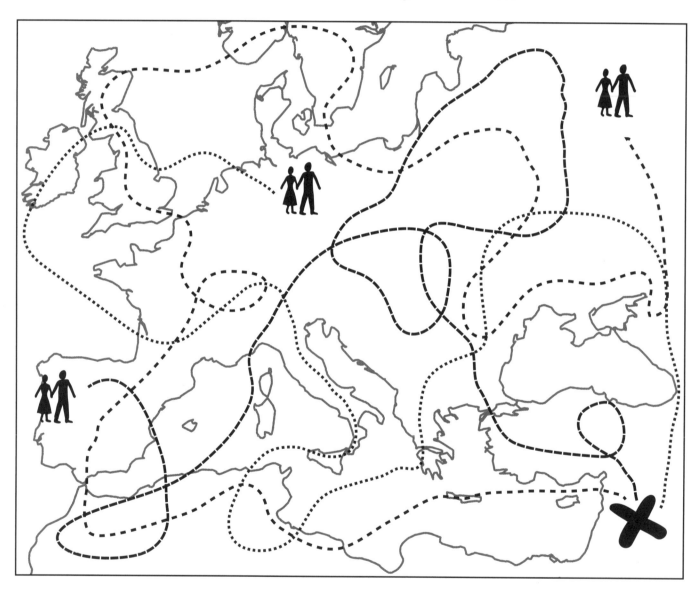

Your Own Masterpiece

Draw a picture of a missionary presenting a newly translated Bible to a tribal chief.

Creative Fun with History!

Acting-Up History:

"Isms" Defined

Cast: Narrator, Peanut Gallery (at least 2 people), Helper #1, Helper #2

Narrator: Today we will talk and learn about schisms;
Today will teach you the facts about "-isms."
Now "-isms" are often quite hard to define,
So I need to have helpers to show us with rhyme!

Helper #1: I'll help! I'll help!

Narrator: Okay. Helper #1, your " -ism" is "fascism."
(pronounced FASH-is-um) (Narrator & Helper #1 put their heads together for a brief conference.)

Helper #1: Oh, I get it!
(to audience) My "-ism," Fascism, Is like this defined:
It doesn't like others, But likes its own kind.
(adds without rhythm, but in great emotional agitation)
Unless, of course, they disagree . . . or believe in God
. . . or help others . . . or . . . or . . . or . . . or . . .
or . . . *(speaking faster and faster)*
(resuming poise) "Master race" was their claim,
But, you know, that's not right.
God Himself made us—We're precious in His sight!

Narrator: Ahem. Yes. As I was saying . . . Fascism once was a famous idea
That Hitler had stuck in his head.
It said, "We're the best, yes, the greatest of all,"
But it made others quite sick with dread.
It said, "We are strong, no one EVER could beat us!"
A boast that we'll see was proved wrong.
It gagged all the press and the churches and people,
And printed lies all the day long.
Now for our next "-ism."

Helper #2: I'll help! I'll help!

Narrator: Okay. Helper #2, your " -ism" is "communism."

Helper #2: Oh, I get it!
(to audience) Com—you know—is . . . um
Is my job to explain. It makes people equal—
'Cept those who complain!
(adds without rhythm, but in great emotional agitation)

The people in charge were not equal either—
They got more than all the others combined!
(in rhythm) "God is dead!" was their claim,
But that's wrongly contrived.
Jesus died for our sins, And He rose, He's ALIVE!

Narrator: Ahem. Yes. Furthermore . . .
Communism once was a famous idea
That came from Karl Marx's thick head.
It claimed, "We all share everything that we've got,"
But some share more often, 'twas said.
It also gagged presses, thought much of itself,
And wanted to take o'er the world.
It fashioned great armies and navies and airplanes,
And showed its flag flying unfurled.

Peanut Gallery: *(scratch their heads in unison)*
Excuse us, oh pardon, but we really don't see
The difference between them. Oh, won't you agree
They're both really icky and proud and revolting.
But how are they different? We're listening and noting.

Narrator: Ahem, ah, yes, good question . . .
Helper #1, Helper #2, can you please demonstrate?
OK, now, pay attention—here's the rhyme and the mime!
Fascism wants just the RIGHT kind of people.
(Helper #1, by pointing at Peanut Gallery, chooses one, rejects another)
Communism says all the workers are equal.
(Helper #2, by pointing, forcefully puts Peanut Gallery in line)
Both of them hate God, *(both Helpers shake their fists upwards)* and favor the leaders, *(both Helpers pat themselves on the back)* and lie, *(both Helpers point at each other)* cheat, *(both Helpers put other hand behind back and smile fake smiles)* and steal. *(both Helpers, using pointing hand, pretend to take something)*
Now, beware all you readers! *(both Helpers point to the audience)*

Peanut Gallery: A-ha! 0-ho! Ee-he! We see! Yes, indeed!
(all nod their heads in agreement)

Narrator: There are other "-isms"
That someday you should know,
But enough is enough.
Now, you really must go! *(everyone scatter offstage)*

World War II & Deliverances

Miracle at Dunkirk

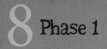

Bible Verses to Read & Talk About

How to Conduct a War: Proverbs 20:18, 24:6

The Allies needed great wisdom to know how to fight against Hitler—and win! Read these Scripture passages together and talk about what you learn.

What do these Scriptures say is necessary if one is going to wage war?

Why do you think the Bible even talks about how to conduct a war? What do you think might have happened if Hitler had won World War II?

Suggested Books & Videos for the Whole Family

WWII by Ken Hills

This is an excellent "primer" for children about WWII. From the Wars That Changed the World series, this volume includes all of the major fronts of the war.

Dunkirk by R. Conrad Stein

Read about the Miracle at Dunkirk where more than 300,000 Allied soldiers were saved off the beach at Dunkirk by an unlikely fleet of vessels. A fabulous book in the World at War series!

Twenty and Ten by Claire Huchet Bishop

The incredible, true story of a French school in WWII under German occupation that decides to hide ten Jewish refugee children. There is also a video of this story, entitled _Miracle at Moreaux_. Highly recommended! Great read-aloud.

People in History by R. J. Unstead

A wonderful Series of short biographies, this book begins with the Roman invasion of Britain and continues through WWII. It's written for younger children, though even adults will find it informative.

Flight of the Fugitives by Dave & Neta Jackson

Historical fiction for children in the Trailblazer Books series, this is the story of Gladys Aylward and her mission in China before and during WWII. Highly recommended!

The Inn of the Sixth Happiness (video)

The story of Gladys Aylward, this movie is somewhat romanticized for Hollywood, but it is an excellent portrayal of the conditions Gladys faced. Great for the whole family!

Fascinating Folks & Exciting Events

WWII (1939–1945)

At the end of World War I, an armistice was signed that brought the fighting to a halt. But it took the signing of a treaty to fully end the war. This treaty was called the Treaty of Versailles (pronounced "vere-sigh"), and it was very harsh to the German people. You see, the Allies were very angry with Germany for WWI, and they intended to have the Germans punished. So, they demanded that Germany pay $33 billion

to the Allies (to pay for the war); the German army was limited to 100,000 soldiers; and the German navy was reduced to six warships, along with other penalties. This was very hard on the German people. Remember, their country was devastated by the war, too.

In this difficult time, a man began to tell the people that these problems were not their fault; that the Treaty of Versailles was wrong; that Germany would be great again; and that the real troublemakers in Germany were the Jewish people. This man was Adolf Hitler. Many people liked what he had to say, and he began to rise in power. Eventually, he became the leader of Germany and began to set his strange ideas in motion. He began to build up the army, the navy, and the air force. He forced Jewish people to wear yellow stars on their clothing so others could recognize that they were Jewish—and persecute them. He got rid of his enemies in one terrible night. Then he began to take over other countries. First, he took Austria—and no one did anything to stop him. Next, he took Czechoslovakia— and no one did anything to stop him. However, when he took Poland in September, 1939, Great Britain and France declared war. There was no fighting that winter, but in May, 1940, the Germans suddenly and terrifyingly invaded Holland, Belgium, and France. France signed an armistice with Germany in the very train car that the armistice of WWI was signed in! That left Great Britain to fight Germany alone!

Hitler wanted to take over Great Britain, too, but there was a problem—the English Channel prevented him from bringing his tanks and troops to England. He bombed England from airplanes to "soften them up" and make them surrender. However, the new leader in England, Winston Churchill, had a motto: "Never give in!" And he didn't.

Hitler grew frustrated trying to conquer the British isles, so he turned his sights to Russia. Though Hitler was a fascist (German fascists were called "Nazis") and was totally opposed to communism, he had signed a peace agreement with Communist Russia when he invaded Poland. Now, he changed his mind and wanted to conquer Russia. Eventually, Russia conquered Hitler in the same way she had conquered Napoleon.

Over on the other side of the world, Japan (aligned with Germany and Italy) attacked the U.S. Naval Base at Pearl Harbor in Hawaii. So, the U.S. entered the war on the side of Great Britain and the Allies. Whew! What a mess! The whole world was at war: in Europe, Hitler was in control (except for Great Britain); in Asia and the Pacific, Japan was taking over islands and countries (like the Philippines); in North Africa, the Germans and Italians were pushing through Egypt trying to take Palestine—where many European Jews had taken refuge to escape Hitler; and on and on. In the midst of all these battles, Hitler was also working on his "Final Solution"—eliminating all the Jewish people, as well as Gypsies, Slavs, and Russians, from Europe. It was a very scary time!

Things eventually began to go wrong for Hitler: he lost in Russia; he lost in Africa; and then, on D-Day, the Allies invaded Europe through France. After a miraculous deliverance for the Allies in the Pacific, the Japanese began to lose there, as well. Finally, in 1945, the Germans surrendered in Europe and the Japanese surrendered in Asia. The most destructive, devastating war in world history was finally over.

Word Search

Using the words from your vocabulary list at the bottom of the page, search for words in the puzzle. The words are diagonal, vertical, and horizontal. Have fun!

```
P A N Z E R S F P E A R L H A R B O R
D O H P L F R R B L I T U K R I F F U
H U F L E E T O L T W F F I M F C M N
C A N E S E P G I T P A T R I R A P D
H H R C L A A M T M A T W K S O M D E
I A U B M R R E Z I R O A C T G A C R
N E H R O I A N K R A M F O I Y O U G
T C O N C E N T R A T I O N C A M P R
E K L P D H K P I C R C I C E A U D O
R I O E Z D H E E L O A T E Z B K U U
C N C A Y O A I G E O G J N B O M M N
E T A R N R E S L U P E T R L M R K D
S E U Y R A I O N L E R E D E B E I J
S R S M T T L I B E R A T E E C S R F
O C T E C N J L U F T W A F F E C K R
R E S I S T A N C E J O N E T M U G O
```

armistice	D-Day	liberate	phony
Atomic Age	Dunkirk	Luftwaffe	rescue
blitzkrieg	fleet *(navy term)*	miracle	Resistance
bomb	frogmen	Panzers	underground *(as in the Resistance)*
Churchill	Holocaust	paratrooper	
concentration camp	intercessor	Pearl Harbor	

Hands-On History Fun

Create-A-Craft:

Origami Puppet

Japan was on the side of Germany and Italy during World War II. They fought in the Pacific region and nearly succeeded in winning! The Japanese emperor decided that the Japanese nation needed to surrender to the Allies after two atomic bombs were dropped on Japanese cities.

Origami, which is a Japanese word meaning "folded paper," has delighted people for centuries. Try your hand at folding this paper puppet.

You will need:

* 1 square of Origami paper per student (approximately 5" x 5")

First, with the color side down (if you have one-side colored paper), fold the paper across diagonally. Unfold. Now fold the paper across diagonally the other direction. Unfold. Look at the paper. Do you see the center point that has been created by folding? Now, fold each of the four corners of the paper in to the center point. You will have a smaller square. Hold onto the folds, but turn the square over, and repeat the step of folding the four corners in to the center point. Your square now is quite small. Now, looking at the square, fold the top half down to the bottom half. This will expose four small flaps at the center. Place your thumb and three of your fingers into the flaps (one per flap). Carefully spread the paper open—and, voila! You have a puppet!

Fun Food to Fix:

Keep-'Em-Warm Cocoa

During the rescue of the Allied forces from the beaches of Dunkirk after Germany invaded Holland, Belgium, and France, the soldiers and sailors got wet and cold. This tasty drink will remind you of how comforting hot cocoa would have been to them!

You will need for each serving:

* 1 tablespoon cocoa
* 2 tablespoons sugar
* 1 cup milk
* Pinch of salt
* ⅛ teaspoon vanilla
* 1 marshmallow

CAUTION: ADULT SUPERVISION REQUIRED. Place the marshmallow in a mug. Place the cocoa, sugar, and salt in a saucepan. Add enough milk to the cocoa to make a paste. Using a wire whip, stir this paste, then while stirring, add the rest of the milk. Heat just to the boiling point. As soon as bubbles appear, remove from the heat. Add the vanilla. Have an adult pour the hot cocoa over the marshmallow in the mug. Yum!

Where in the World?

... was the Normandy Invasion on D-Day?

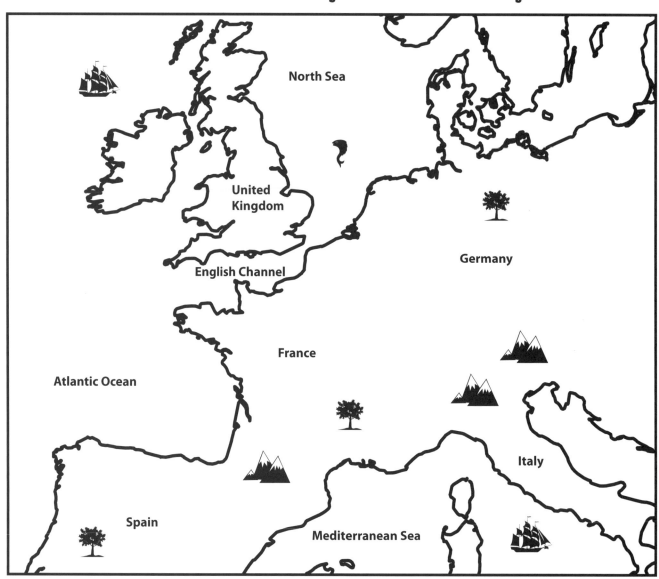

Color the areas around these:

purple mountains   **green vegetation**   **blue water**

Clues for finding Normandy, where the Allied forces invaded on D-Day

- My beaches are on the NORTH coast of France.
- I am SOUTH of the U.K.
- I point NORTH into the English Channel.

Where am I?

Your Own Masterpiece

Draw a picture of a German tank in the North African desert.

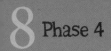
Creative Fun with History!

Going Goofy Games:

Save the Lads at Dunkirk!
A game where the little guys win.

When Hitler's forces invaded Holland, Belgium, and France, they moved VERY quickly! In fact, it was called a "blitzkrieg," or lightning war. The Allied soldiers would have all been captured—350,000 of them—except for the English fleet of little boats and tug boats and yachts and ferries and all kinds of unlikely, unusual floating devices! For nine days, the Germans stopped their tanks and troops while the German Air Force, flying through an amazing fog and smoke cover, tried to find the boats and bomb them. When it was all over, 338,000 Allied soldiers had been saved. What a miracle!

You will need:

- 2 teams: put all the bigger, stronger players on the GA team with an equal number of smaller players on the EF team. (Feel free to adjust the rules to keep the GA team handicapped.)
  - » EF team—English fleet—starts behind the boundary on the west side
  - » GA team—German army—starts behind the boundary on the east side
- Paper plates marked "BEF," which stands for British Expeditionary Force
- Two plates per player on the EF—English Fleet Team
- 2 pieces of rope for boundaries—20 feet apart, more or less, depending on the teams

EF team lines up at Dover facing Dunkirk across the English Channel. GA team lines up at Dunkirk facing Dover across the English Channel.

Lay the paper plates marked "BEF" on the floor just inches from the GA boundary.

Play starts when one person from the EF team runs to the Dunkirk line and grabs one paper plate. The GA appoints a chaser to try to tag the EF runner, but, before releasing the chaser, the GA must all together loudly chant, "Clouds! Smoke! Fog! Can't see!" Immediately, then, the GA player may try to tag the EF player who is dashing back to the EF side.

If the GA chaser catches the runner, the runner has to stand on the side of the GA team as a "POW" (prisoner of war). If the chaser does NOT catch the runner before the runner makes it back to Dover, then the chaser has to stand on the side of the EF team as a POW.

Then the next EF runner runs to Dunkirk, and the GA team chants again before releasing the next chaser.

When all the EF players have a had a chance to run to Dunkirk, it is time to do a prisoner exchange. The EF team may redeem as many of its players held as POWs as they have GA POWs to trade in exchange.

After the prisoner exchange, the EF begins saving the BEF (paper plates) once again. Again, after all the EF team members (who are not POWs) have run to Dunkirk a second time, do another prisoner exchange.

Whoever has the most free team members (not POWs) at the end of Round Two wins the game.

Remember that, though Hitler claimed a military victory, the free world was the winner because those 338,000 Allied soldiers who were rescued off the beaches of Dunkirk were the lads who would come back and fight in Europe again at D-Day.

Revivals & Revolutions

Smuggling Bibles at
Checkpoint Charlie

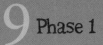

Bible Verses to Read & Talk About

The Nation of Israel: Psalm 126; Isaiah 35:10, 43:5–7

In May of 1948, the United Nations voted to allow the modern nation of Israel to be formed in Palestine. After almost 1900 years (from 70 AD–1948 AD), the Jewish people again had a homeland. Read these Scripture passages together and talk about what you learn.

How does the Bible describe the response of the people when they are able to return to Israel? Even though these Scriptures describe the return from Babylonian captivity, it was also descriptive of the 1948 rebirth of Israel. Why do you think it made the Jewish people so happy? What had their experience been like in Germany? In Russia?

A Biblical Response to Enemies: Matthew 5:43–48

Corrie ten Boom was a Dutch watchmaker who was imprisoned during World War II for helping Jewish people. Her father and sister were also arrested with her, and both of them died during their captivity. Yet God was able to use Corrie after WWII to bring hope and healing to the people of Germany and the world because she responded biblically to her situation. Read this Scripture passage together and talk about what you learn.

What does the Bible say we should do about our enemies? Is that different from what the world thinks? How is it different? How is it possible to obey the Bible's command?

Suggested Books for Reading Together

The Arab/Israeli Conflict by Paul J. Deegan

The situation in the Middle East is complex and many faceted. This book describes many of the issues in terms children can understand.

God's Smuggler by Brother Andrew

We read this book out loud when our children were young, talking with them about the importance of having God's Word. It's a wonderful, true adventure story about a man who obeyed God and saw amazing results take place. Highly recommended! Great read-aloud.

Israel by Don Foy

This Festivals of the World title is a wonderful way to introduce younger children to the festivals of modern day Israel. Learn about how this nation celebrates Memorial Day and Independence Day, as well as about the forest of six million trees planted in memory of those who died in the Holocaust.

Assassins in the Cathedral by Dave & Neta Jackson

This is historical fiction of Festo Kivengere, bishop in Uganda during Idi Amin's regime. This Trailblazer Books title will not only help your students understand some of the difficulties faced by the African countries, such as warring tribes living side by side, but it will show the profound importance of forgiveness. Excellent!

Fascinating Folks & Exciting Events

Jim Elliot (1927–1956)

Many people who serve the Lord as missionaries today trace their decision to become a missionary back to the effect Jim Elliot had upon them. Who was this amazingly influential servant of God? He was born in Oregon, the son of a Bible teacher/evangelist. During his time at Wheaton College, Jim felt the call of God to work in pioneer missions in South America. To prepare, he studied Greek in college to equip himself for translating the Scriptures, he became a college wrestler to strengthen his body for pioneer work, and he prayed that other people would be called to pioneer missions with him—and God answered those prayers! Jim thought a lot about serving the Lord fully, about giving his life to fulfill God's purposes. He wrote, "Wherever you are, be ALL there. Live to the hilt every situation you believe to be the will of God." And that is just what he did! Whether he was studying, wrestling, preaching, playing, praying . . . he did it to the hilt.

While Jim was still in college, he learned about a tribe of people living deep in the jungles of Ecuador. They were known as the Aucas. These people were very fierce. They killed anyone, white or native, who came into their territory. Jim's heart was moved by God's compassion for this "unreached people," and he began to pray that God would open the door for him to share the gospel with them. When he reached South America, Jim began to work with the Quichua Indians by learning their language, building a mission station, and discipling the young Christian converts. In 1953, he married his college sweetheart, Elisabeth, and together they worked diligently in the jungle. However, he continued to pray for the Aucas.

In 1955, a Missionary Aviation Fellowship pilot named Nate Saint spotted an Auca settlement from the air. This was *very* exciting news to Jim and his friends because it was quite rare to find this people group. So they began flying over the settlement and dropping gifts for the people. They were attempting to show that they were friendly and that they wanted to make contact. After months of doing this, the missionaries believed the time had come to actually meet the tribal people. Jim and four other missionary men flew into the jungle and landed on a river beach close to the settlement. They were very excited when an Auca man and two women came to their landing site, because the missionaries could try to communicate that they wanted to be friends. However, two days later, a group of Auca warriors came to the landing site and killed all five missionaries.

That is very sad, but that was not the end of the story. God was at work in the Auca tribe! The missionaries had carried rifles with them, but they chose not to defend themselves because they had come in peace to bring God's Word to the Aucas. When the warriors learned that, they were stunned! No one in their tribe had ever heard of such a thing! This was the key that opened their hearts to the message of the gospel.

Isn't it amazing to know that these fierce warriors and many others of their tribe became Christians? And to know that Jim Elliot's widow, Elisabeth, and Nate Saint's sister, Rachel, lived as missionaries among the Auca people for many years? And to know that Nate Saint's son and daughter were baptized in the river by two of the Christian warriors right near the spot where they had killed the children's father nine years earlier? And to know that these people are growing in Christian faith and obedience? Jim Elliot wrote, "He is no fool who gives what he cannot keep to gain what he cannot lose." Amen!

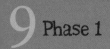

Korean War (1950–1953)

At the end of World War II, many countries looked different. One country, Korea, had been under Japanese control since 1895, but it was released from Japanese occupation at the end of the war. The Allies decided to divide the country in half for a short time—the U.S. helping the folks in the South and the Soviet Russians helping the folks in the North. They were *supposed* to leave after an election was held to select a government for Korea. Unfortunately, the folks in the North didn't like what the folks in the South voted for, and vice versa. So the North Korean army attacked South Korea. Well, this was very upsetting to the U.S. and to the United Nations (a new group of representatives from around the world trying to solve international issues without going to war). So they sent lots of soldiers, tanks, airplanes, and navy ships to help the South Koreans. Then the war went the other direction, and the South Koreans (plus U.S. and other U.N. soldiers) attacked North Korea. At this point, it got really messy. The Chinese (who were just north of North Korea) joined in the battle on the side of the North Koreans. The U.N. forces kept the Chinese forces at the middle point of the country (just about where the division had been made originally), but the two sides could not agree on how to end the fighting. They finally signed an armistice; however, they never signed a treaty. That is why, forty years later, there are still U.S. soldiers patrolling the "demilitarized zone" between North and South Korea!

Crack the Code

Using the key provided below, decode your vocabulary list. For each letter given, find it in the crossbars and replace it with the letter opposite it, so A becomes D, E becomes G, F becomes H, and so on. The first one has been done for you.

agbmimplydqlmp decolonization

ndsqlqlmp partition

Ndigrqlpg Palestine

Lrsdgi Israel

Jmsgd Korea

Cgsilp Udii Berlin Wall

Odm Mao

odsbf march

Bmia Uds Cold War

Bmoowplrq Cimb Communist bloc

roweeig smuggle

Csmqfgs Dpasgu Brother Andrew

Wplqga Pdqlmpr United Nations

dlsilhq airlift

Lsmp Bwsqdlp Iron Curtain

sghwegg refugee

gogselpe emerging

ilolqga uds limited war

bmsswnqlmp corruption

airlift	Communist bloc	Iron Curtain	Mao	refugee
Berlin Wall	corruption	Israel	march	smuggle
Brother Andrew	decolonization	Korea	Palestine	United Nations
Cold War	emerging	limited war	partition	

Hands-On History Fun

Create-A-Craft:

Make this "He's Got the Whole World in His Hands" Globe

As we finish off our studies of *World Empires, World Missions, World Wars*, it is important to remember that God is still sending missionaries out across the globe! As you make this craft, be sure to sing the song.

This craft will take two separate sessions. Any remaining paste at the end of Session 1 can be stored in a sealed plastic container and reused for Session 2.

You will need:

- 1 round balloon per student

- Papier-mâché paste (recipe follows)

- Green tissue paper, torn into strips 8" to 12" long

- Blue tissue paper, torn into strips 8" to 12" long

- String for hanging the drying globes

- Real globe to look at while you make your own (optional)

Papier-mâché Paste:

- ¼ cup white flour

- 1 cup water, room temperature

- 5 more cups water in a saucepan

CAUTION: ADULT SUPERVISION REQUIRED. Mix the flour and the first cup of water in a bowl, making sure there are no lumps of flour. Bring the five cups of water to a boil in a large saucepan. When it boils, carefully stir the flour and water mixture into the boiling water. Stir constantly, while still boiling, for about five minutes. Let the mixture cool.

Session 1:

Protect your working surface with lots of newspaper or a large board. Be sure to wear an apron or old clothes! Inflate the balloon and tie a knot. This will be the top of the globe. Now, dip a strip of blue tissue paper into the paste and lay it on the balloon. Continue, slowly but surely, to cover the balloon completely with blue tissue paper, leaving only the balloon knot visible. Tie a piece of string around the balloon knot and hang the globe up to dry.

Session 2:

Protect your working surface with lots of newspaper or a large board. Be sure to wear an apron or old clothes! Dip a strip of green tissue into the paste and lay it on the blue globe to represent land. You may want to look at a globe as you do this part, but you can also use your imagination! Continue to add green tissue paper to the globe until you have both water (blue tissue) and land (green tissue). Hang your globe up to dry. Then, when it is dry, find a place to display it where you will be reminded to pray for missionaries all over the world!

Fun Food to Fix:

Smuggled Chocolate in Peanut Butter Balls

Brother Andrew, during the Cold War, began smuggling Bibles to people in Communist lands where Bibles were forbidden. It brought hope and encouragement to believers in these places to know that they were not forgotten and that God had provided His Word for them. Brother Andrew's Scripture verse from God was "Strengthen that which remains."

You will need:

- 1 cup peanut butter
- ⅓ cup nonfat dry milk
- ¼ cup honey
- ½ cup coconut
- ¼ cup sesame seeds
- Small chocolate pieces or large chocolate chips

Form into balls. With your finger, make a hole in each ball. Push the chocolate pieces into the center, then reform the ball. Make sure the chocolate is invisible. Roll in sesame seeds. See if anyone notices that you are smuggling chocolate in the Peanut Butter Balls!

Where in the World?

. . . are North and South Korea?

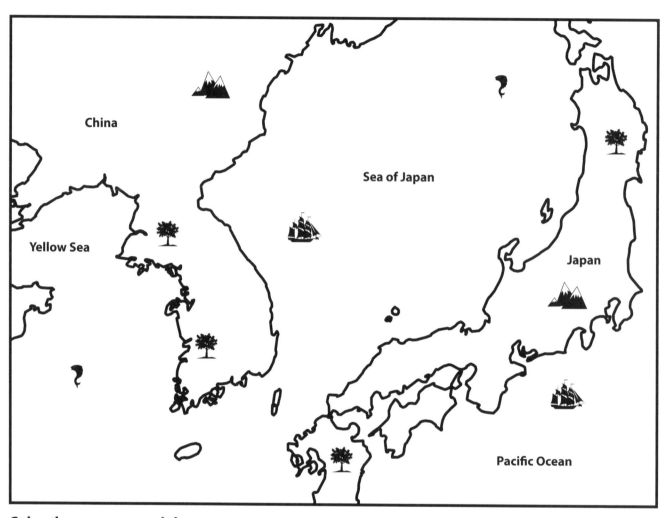

Color the areas around these:

 purple mountains

green vegetation

 blue water

Clues for finding North and South Korea:

- We are on a peninsula.
- We are EAST of the Yellow Sea.

Where are we?

- We are SOUTH of China.
- We are WEST of the Sea of Japan.

Your Own Masterpiece

Draw a picture of where YOU would like to go on a missions trip with your family.

Creative Fun with History!

Singing Somewhat Silly Songs:

Missionaries 'Round the Globe

(to the tune of "Old MacDonald Had a Farm")

Chorus:

Missionaries 'round the globe. E-I-E-I-0
Lookin' for new spots to probe. E-I-E-I-0

With a bapt'sm here, and a church built there,
Here they are, there they go,
Every creature, high and low.
Missionaries 'round the globe.
E-I-E-I-0

Chorus

In Cuba here, and Chile there,
Congo, Cyprus,
Cameroon, Cambodia.
Missionaries 'round the globe.
E-I-E-I-0

Chorus

In Ecuador here, and Haiti there,
Iran, India,
Indonesia, Israel.
Missionaries 'round the globe.
E-I-E-I-0

Chorus

Morocco here, Mongolia there,
Maldives, Mali,
Mauritania, Mexico.
Missionaries 'round the globe.
E-I-E-I-0

Chorus

In Nepal here, and Niger there,
Pakistan, Paraguay,
And Papua New Guinea.
Missionaries 'round the globe.
E-I-E-I-0

Chorus

In Syria here, and Sudan there,
Singapore, Senegal
Saudi Arabia.
Missionaries 'round the globe.
E-I-E-I-0

Chorus

In Tonga here, and Togo there,
Turkey, Taiwan
Trinidad, Tunisia.
Missionaries 'round the globe.
E-I-E-I-0

Chorus

Uganda here and Yemen there,
Zaire, Zimbabwe,
Venezuela, Vietnam.
Missionaries 'round the globe.
E-I-E-I-0

Chorus

With airplanes here, and satellites there,
With cell phones, fax machines
And everything in between!
Missionaries 'round the globe.
E-I-E-I-0